HEALTH IS MADE AT HOME
HOSPITALS ARE FOR REPAIRS

SALUS Global Knowledge Exchange
West Suite, Westgate Court
17 Western Road
Billericay
Essex CM12 9DY
United Kingdom

www.salus.global
info@salus.global

SALUS Global Knowledge Exchange is a division of Sansom & Sansom Associates Ltd.
SALUS is a global media, publishing, research, events and training organisation with
a vision to improve human and planetary health by design. Our mission is to create,
share and disseminate knowledge concerning the relationship between human health
and the natural, built and social environment.

Brand development and design by Brandality.

Printed in the UK by The Magazine Printing Company, a part of Stephens
& George Ltd.

A catalogue record for this publication is available from the British Library.

ISBN 978-1-83-803130-5
eISBN 978-1-83-803-131-2

www.healthismadeathome.uk

HEALTH IS MADE AT HOME HOSPITALS ARE FOR REPAIRS

BUILDING A HEALTHY AND HEALTH-CREATING SOCIETY

NIGEL CRISP

SALUS
GLOBAL KNOWLEDGE EXCHANGE

For Summer and Marney

CONTENTS

PART ONE

INTRODUCTION

CHAPTER ONE

INTRODUCTION

I began this book long before the pandemic struck. I wanted to celebrate the thousands of people such as teachers, employers, community leaders, architects and entrepreneurs who are not health professionals but who are actively improving health and wellbeing. And I wanted to understand what they were doing and explore what it meant for the future.

Health is made at home is a journey of discovery. It describes how each of us can create health, improve our communities and take pressure off the NHS so it is always there when we need it.

The pandemic has undoubtedly reinforced the importance of this whole approach and shown us more clearly the different roles played in health by the NHS, government, and by each of us as citizens and members of society.

The NHS has been fighting for our lives for the past few weeks and months. Throwing all its resources at the pandemic. Millions of health and care workers have been magnificent, rising to the occasion with bravery and skill. It has demonstrated, among other things, that we must support and resource them better for the future.

Government has also had a crucial role to play: providing leadership and direction, introducing emergency legislation, and supporting the NHS and the economy. There will be many lessons to learn from this experience about preparedness and the role of government in future health emergencies.

And it's been up to us, the general public, how far and how fast the virus spreads. Our behaviour has mattered. And millions have volunteered to help, kept community and voluntary activity going, or simply looked after our neighbours. Millions more have kept the vital non-health emergency and other services running in agriculture, retail, delivery, power, transport, finance, rubbish collection and so much more. We have all had our part to play.

Looking forward, there will continue to be a vital role for us all in health when the pandemic is over because the NHS can't do everything by itself. The NHS can't deal with many of today's major health problems such as loneliness, stress, obesity, poverty and addictions. It can only really react, doing the repairs but not addressing the underlying causes.

There are people all over the country who are tackling these causes in their homes, workplaces and communities. The leaders and pioneers. People like the Berkshire teachers working with children excluded from school, the unemployed men in Salford improving their community, the bankers tackling mental health in the City, and many others.

They are opening up new ideas about health creation and quality of life and showing us what they mean in practice. Not waiting for government or health professionals to tell them what to do. Breaking new ground, taking the initiative and leading. They are not just preventing disease but creating health.

These are not merely developments on past practice, tweaks to the system or incremental change. They are not simply about clinicians starting to prescribe healthy activities as well as medicines. Nor are they about the NHS beginning actively to pursue prevention and promotion. Or engaging the public. Welcome as these things are, they maintain the control of the system and the professionals. And they keep us dependent on them. Business as usual.

There is a much more radical change underway. A dislocation, a shift in power and control. Health professionals don't create our health. We do. All of us as individuals have responsibilities for our own health and often for the health of our families. Our behaviour, diet, exercise and use of tobacco and alcohol all affect our health and wellbeing.

And employers, educators, architects, businesses and community leaders, as well as government, also have a responsibility to create the conditions that allow us to live healthy lives.

Government policies can support or damage all these initiatives. Growing inequalities, the effects of years of austerity, and poverty – above all – damage health. Sir Michael Marmot, the leading epidemiologist, has argued cogently that we need better policies and a fairer society if we are to tackle the health gap between rich and poor and improve health for all. Government policy is vital. Lord Gus O'Donnell, the former cabinet secretary, argues that governments should shape policies and measure progress in terms of their impact on improving wellbeing. This seems even more important now.

And, as the Covid-19 pandemic has shown, governments need to be much better at long term thinking and planning.

As individuals, organisations and communities begin to do more to shape their own health, we will see a whole new framework developing with different ways of doing things, better use of technology, different relationships and changed power structures.

There are other equally profound changes happening in the wider world, both nationally and globally. As women at last begin to move towards taking their rightful place in the world, it won't be business as usual. A society of women and men leaders will be a different society, with different norms and behaviours. And it may bring with it a greater emphasis on health and wellbeing.

UK politics is changing, too, and needs to find new ways of responding to the deep divisions in our society, which have been exacerbated in recent years by Brexit. The pandemic has revealed to us all some of the hidden truths about our society. The migrant workers who do so many of the lowest paid and insecure jobs, the millions on zero hours contracts with no support, the poverty and inequality, and the way different ethnic groups have been affected.

We may all have been in this together but it has impacted us very differently. And, it is making us confront the uncomfortable reality that the *old normal* was bad for many people.

***

Globally, climate change and the emergence of a new multi-polar world are changing attitudes and behaviour and the very way we see the world. And technology will play an important part for both good and ill.

We have finally reached the end of the long 20th century and we need to discover and develop the new ideas and technologies that will enable us to prosper in the 21st.

Health is made at home is designed to illustrate what is already happening. To tell just a few of the stories of the many pioneering leaders in health, education, business, architecture and communities – the health creators – and to accelerate the change that is underway.

All of them have been affected by the pandemic. Some of the organisations and businesses described here have had to close down at least temporarily, some have adapted what they do, and others have developed new programmes. Some may not survive while others will find new opportunities and a new future. But this virus won't kill off the change that is underway.

These pioneers give us hope that, despite all the problems and pressures, we can build a better and more equal society, where people have greater autonomy and control over their health and wellbeing and where they can live lives they have reason to value.

The NHS has been changing, too, adapting to the new situation with greater use of technology, better teamwork and swift decision making – and it is determined to maintain the gains it has made during this very difficult period. And the Government has taken on new and more interventionist roles in society that, come what may, will be with us for many years to come.

The damage, too, will have long term consequences: lives lost and ruined, a massive backlog for other treatments, mental health problems for the public and health and care workers alike, and economic damage that will bring its own health and financial consequences.

Now, however, with our world disrupted by the pandemic, is the right time for us to act.

Health is made at home identifies ten big lessons we should learn from the health creators and ten government policies that need to change or be adopted. It calls for a new partnership between the health creators, the NHS and government.

And it ends with a commitment to action from many of the groups described here. And a challenge to the NHS and the Government to join them in building a healthy and health-creating society.

It starts by challenging us to leave behind our assumptions about health, to stop seeing health through the lens of the NHS – *taking off our NHS spectacles* – and begin to see the world differently.

CHAPTER TWO

TAKING OFF OUR NHS SPECTACLES

Life has changed since the NHS was created more than 70 years ago. Many of today's biggest health problems such as loneliness, stress, obesity, poverty and addictions simply can't be tackled by the NHS alone. It can only react, doing the repairs but not dealing with the underlying causes.

Put simply, we are trying to deal with today's problems with a health system that was designed to tackle yesterday's diseases. It is no wonder there are so many difficulties. We need a fundamental change of direction and a new way of thinking about health and wellbeing.

This is not just about prevention or health promotion. Nor just about government policies. Health and wellbeing are about so much more than the absence of disease. They are about life and freedom, being all that we can be, and living life to the full. They are about our relationships, how we live, and what happens to us at work and at school. And they are about confidence and control, and the quality of our lives.

Because of this, our health as individuals is intimately connected to the health of our communities and our society – and, ultimately, our environment and our planet.

And if we get this right, we will not only improve our lives but also take some of the pressure off the NHS and make sure it is always there when we need it.

***

As I write, we are all focused on fighting Covid-19 and these efforts will need to continue for many months. We already know that the virus will leave behind significant mental and physical health problems. Some of this will be due to the trauma of the deaths and the difficult working environment, some due to the effects of isolation, and some because so many treatments and operations for other conditions have been put on hold. We also know that there will be health consequences from the economic collapse with more people out of work and in poverty. And, that different parts of the population will be affected differently.

The impact of the pandemic will be felt for years to come and much of the continuing burden of disease will be in precisely those long term conditions and societal problems that the NHS can't deal with by itself.

Yet the way we tend to think and talk about health is still mostly about healthcare and hospitals and professionals. We need only remember the 2019 election to see that the politicians and media believed that voters would respond to promises of new hospitals, more nurses and GPs, and more money for the NHS.

And it's still too often about things done to us or for us, not by us.

When, we might ask, did we decide to hand over control of our health almost entirely to the professionals and to follow all their rules? And why do we so often feel that we are being made to fit into the system rather than it fitting around us?

Isn't it time to change all this, time for us to assert ourselves as equal partners with the NHS and the state?

In fact, it is now urgent that we do so because the NHS won't be able to cope, however valiantly it tries and however many new hospitals are built.

Today's health problems are very different from those that the NHS had to tackle when it was founded in 1948. Then, people were much more likely to die of infections, in childbirth, in factory accidents, and on the operating table, and there was no relief from arthritic hips, cataracts, blocked arteries and damaged heart valves. Old age really did start at 65 and death often followed fairly soon afterwards. It was a very different world.

Today, there has been near miraculous progress. We are healthier and life expectancy has increased by almost a quarter. That means on average almost 15 more years for each of us. Better sanitation, housing, social benefits and education have all played their part. And new drugs and therapies are now bringing many of the most frightening diseases under control.

There is the promise of much more to come, with genetics, artificial intelligence (AI), pharmacology and new technologies holding out the hope of personalised precision medicine and the cure for all our ills. And in many of these areas, the UK is leading the way with some of the most vibrant AI, biotech and life sciences companies in the world.

But that's not the whole story, and perhaps not even the bigger part. The Covid-19 pandemic has jolted us out of any complacency we may have had about the risks from infections. TB is resurgent, HIV/AIDS never went away and the threat from new drug resistant infections (antimicrobial resistance) is growing all the time. There will be other pandemics and more localised epidemics with which to contend.

We will need new contingency plans and new measures to tackle these infections in future and they will require all of us and all sectors of society to take responsibility by playing our part.

At the same time, life expectancy is stalling as long term conditions and lifestyle diseases take hold. Loneliness can be a precursor of dementia, stress shortens lives, obesity can lead to diabetes, poverty is linked to cardiac and other diseases, and addictions cause multiple health problems. The pandemic is wreaking havoc but these chronic conditions remain the biggest areas of disease and, in the longer run, will be the greatest cost to the NHS and society. And the NHS can't deal with them by itself.

These problems are made worse by increasing divisions in society, greater stress and insecurity in school and at work, and by growing inequalities. Austerity has created a sense of public neglect while, at the same time, too many private companies and public services now don't seem to care about the individual at all in their pursuit of profits or financial balance. Brexit has revealed old differences and created new ones. It is a toxic mix.

The pandemic has brought us all together in a national fight against the virus. One where we have all had roles to play: the NHS, government, and all the different sectors of the economy and parts of society.

Maybe this experience will help us find a new approach. One that is not constrained by the way we have done things in the past but looks to the future. An approach that offers us new ideas and a new narrative, and opens up new opportunities by going far beyond the NHS and the formal health and care system.

And the timing is perfect.

Public perceptions are already starting to change. The media in recent years have become increasingly full of stories about air pollution, heat stroke, childhood development or the difference in life expectancy between north and south. They reveal how interested we all are in health and wellbeing. They also show that, despite the election rhetoric, we all recognise that health is about how we live our lives and how society is organised, and not just about healthcare and the NHS.

Government policy has shifted in recent years with a new emphasis from the NHS on prevention, active leadership from Public Health England on tackling the causes of ill health, and attempts to engage all government departments in promotion and prevention.

Sir Michael Marmot and colleagues have provided the vital theoretical underpinning by demonstrating how society and social and economic policy affect health and life expectancy. This work has affected professional thinking dramatically in recent years and its influence can be seen throughout *Health is made at home*. Sadly, it has not yet led to significant changes in government policy.

But policy is not everything. Sometimes changes in policy make little difference in reality.

As importantly, there are people and organisations all over the country who are not waiting for changes in government policy but doing something about the problems they see in front of them. These pioneers are taking matters into their hands. Working *with* the professionals but not *for* the professionals. And in some cases, *despite* the professionals. Taking responsibility. Taking a lead. Taking control.

These pioneers, the innovators and leaders – the health creators – are making a difference in their workplaces, schools, towns and communities. They are tackling stress and mental health, providing education and support, promoting physical activity and healthy eating, helping reduce crime, and designing healthy environments – bringing creativity and new ideas to bear in a bottom-up revolution.

And they're not just improving health. They're rebuilding communities as places where people matter, where everyone has something to contribute and where, crucially, we can have greater control over our lives – something we all need to be healthy and fulfilled.

All of us as individuals, of course, are responsible for our own health and often for the health of our families as well. However, we also need the right environment and support. Stress at work can be a killer, but schools can offer pupils the health education they need. Poor housing can ruin our health but space for walking and cycling can offer us many hours of pleasure and extra years of life.

We still, of course, want the NHS to look after us when we need it. The pandemic is a perfect example. It must also be there for accidents, cancers and acute care, and those other truly critical moments in life, as well as playing a bigger role in prevention and promoting health. We also need changes in policy and funding for social care so that older and disabled people and their families can find and afford suitable care when they need it.

And we need the researchers, the scientists, the biotech companies and the clinicians to keep developing new technologies and creating new insights and treatments. They are enabling the health professionals to do the 'repairs' when we need them, and they are also empowering all of us to do far more to prevent disease and promote health.

We are already seeing the beginning of personalised and precision medicine. Clinicians are using new sensors and wearables, such as watches, rings and even clothing, to provide feedback on our health and the progression of disease. Researchers are beginning to identify how the natural environment, music and art influence wellbeing. Scientists are employing big data and machine learning to understand diseases and develop new strategies for prevention as well as for treatment. All this technology can give us far more control – not only to stay healthy but also to allow us to make choices about our treatments and therapies.

But the approach of the health creators goes far beyond the formal health and social care sector, the science and the technology. It requires us to see the world differently and not see everything through the lens of the NHS. In other words, we need to *take off our NHS spectacles*. We need to drop our preconceptions and approach health with an open mind. We need to learn from people in the UK and abroad who aren't constrained by our practices and prejudices and by how things have always been done.

The old African saying *'Health is made at home, hospitals are for repairs'* describes the importance of the home and the community, but it also suggests the even more powerful idea that we can *create* health. And that by getting it right in the home – and in the community, school and workplace – we can create health, resilience, wellbeing and everything that follows from them.

And this book is really all about creating health, by which I mean providing the conditions in which people can be healthy and helping them to be so. It's what a parent does when they care for their child, helping them grow up healthy. And what a good teacher does. And a good employer. All of them exercising a profound and positive influence and helping create a resilient, confident, capable and healthy individual.

As the World Health Organization agreed at its foundation in 1948: *'Health is a state of complete physical, mental and social wellbeing and not merely the absence of disease or infirmity.'*

Or as Dr David Pencheon, a leading public health doctor, said to me: *'We know a lot about the causes of ill health but we don't yet think enough about the causes of health.'* The health creators can help us to learn. This book is a journey of discovery about health and health creation. It describes my meetings with people from all over the country. I have listened to their stories and learned from them about the importance of *creating* health – not just tackling illness but building a truly health-creating society where we can all thrive.

***

My journey started, perhaps surprisingly, in Africa where people face far greater problems than we do in the UK, and where they don't have the NHS and all the other advantages that come from living in one of the richest countries in the world.

People in Africa may not have our resources but they also don't have our vested interests or historical baggage. As a result, they can often be much more innovative and flexible.

It was in Africa where I first learned to take off my NHS spectacles and see the world differently. It was there that I saw things that challenged my own preconceptions about health and health improvement. And, as I describe in Chapter 12, I met some great African health leaders, many of them doctors who have challenged the practices and prejudices of their own profession in order to provide services for their people.

As one of those great leaders, Professor Francis Omaswa, said to me: *'These are our people. We have to do something. We can't just leave them to suffer and die.'*

This strong moral sentiment that *'we have to do something'* echoes throughout this book. It was there in my meetings with the employers in the City of London who are tackling mental illness. It is both good for business and the right thing to do. Mental illness, stress, depression and anxiety have taken over from physical health in recent years to become the biggest health issues in the workplace, costing the economy about £80 million a year but also damaging many thousands of lives.

That moral sentiment is there in the passion of the entrepreneur who is changing the way care is provided and in the determination of the people rebuilding their communities. It is there in the architects designing detention centres and other stressful environments in ways that are human and humane. And in the people fighting inequalities and advocating the rights of minority groups.

It is there even more strongly in the chapters about education, children and young people where I met many deeply passionate people taking on some of the most difficult challenges in our society. And there are, of course, enormous costs here too. Getting it right for children at the start of life can avoid so much expenditure later in life, as well as so much pain and suffering.

There are plenty of people in the UK who challenge us to think differently about health. Disabled people have had to fight to be treated like everyone else and not just as patients or clinical cases. There are also other traditions and disciplines: education, social care or housing, for example, which offer insights and practical solutions to problems. And anthropologists, sociologists, geographers and others are increasingly recognised as having their part to play.

There are several other major themes that recur throughout the book. Good health in older age is largely dependent on having a meaning in life as well as being active socially and physically. These are factors like creativity and the arts, which are important at all stages of life. And my meetings with other pioneers such as the Salford Dadz, a group of largely unemployed men who are improving their housing estate, as well as the Black Health Initiative reinforced for me the importance of communities of all different kinds.

The importance of the natural environment shines throughout, whether in gardens and green spaces in hospitals and housing estates or in the sheer calming effect of greenery and the countryside on adults and children alike. And similarly, the quality of the built environment and the accompanying sense of place, identity and belonging are important for our health and wellbeing.

These health creators all take a broadly entrepreneurial approach, vision led and learning by doing. Many are social and community entrepreneurs while others are in business, melding profit with social benefits – whether in vertical farming, providing care or supporting young parents. All of them are focused on action, making things happen and taking control of the situation as they find it.

The stories in *Health is made at home* are all about remarkable people and organisations, but they are only representative of a far larger group of people who are making a difference everywhere. The more

I looked into what was happening and discussed it, the more I discovered was happening.

There is a great tradition here that long pre-dates the NHS. A tradition that includes the well-known Victorian pioneers Thomas Barnado, Florence Nightingale, William Morris and Octavia Hill, as well as many thousands of others who have over the years worked to improve health. Pioneers in every area, from the Tredegar Working Men's Club and the other precursors of the NHS to the more recent voluntary hospices created over the last 50 years.

And the underlying ideas are not new. Salutogenesis or the creation of health has been written about and researched for years. And there are practical examples such as the Pioneer Health Centre, founded in Peckham in 1926. It had a swimming pool, dance floor, nursery and cafeteria as well as consulting rooms. Ninety years later we have a substantial and growing social prescribing movement where health professionals prescribe activities such as gardening, dance or exercise, rather than medicines. Are we finally catching up with the past?

Life has moved on in so many ways since 1926, with a better educated and more affluent population, greater diversity and advances in technology. But one thing that hasn't changed is that this approach to health creation has still not become mainstream. All this activity hasn't yet changed the way the NHS or government behaves.

Power isn't yet shifting but the will for change is clearly there.

This and the next nine chapters each identify one of the big lessons that we can learn from the health creators. These are the big ideas that will help us change the way we think and act – making this new approach mainstream – and these chapters also describe some of the major policy actions that government needs to take to support this change.

The following four chapters offer a global perspective, bring these big ideas and policy changes together, and look in turn at what they mean for the NHS and government. They also describe recent developments in London and the North of England where social and business entrepreneurs are coming together with local councils and other local bodies to create system-wide change that may well be a model for the future. As Covid-19 has shown, there are roles for the NHS, government and wider society.

The final two chapters consider how this new approach to health and wellbeing fits into the wider social and political landscape of the 21st century, as we at last move on from the attitudes and ideas that shaped the 20th. The book ends with a call to action and a commitment from some of the groups described here to work together to bring about change.

I summarise the impact that the pandemic has had on the activities of the health creators in Chapter 16, and I have included some references to this in earlier chapters.

***

As a former chief executive of the NHS, I know that this change won't be easy or rapid.

The NHS was shaped by the culture, technology and political agreements of the immediate post-war period. This led to a system where doctors and hospitals were dominant, the focus was on treatment not prevention, patients were managed within specialities, and there were organisational and cultural divides between services and institutions. Despite many reforms, these founding conditions remain very powerful to this day.

It is a system that is very successful and cost-effective in dealing with many diseases and problems, and it is still greatly valued by patients. But it is having increasing difficulties in caring for patients with long term and multiple conditions who need care from different agencies and different settings. And it's simply not very good at partnership.

I was not surprised therefore that many of the people I met on my journey admired the skills and knowledge of the health professionals they encountered but felt frustrated in trying to work with the system. They told me that the NHS was closed, self-absorbed, focused on its own priorities, siloed, defensive, and short term in outlook – better at dealing with a clinical emergency than with long term development and partnership planning. And, too often, too political.

But I have also met plenty of people in the NHS who are increasingly frustrated by some of what society expects it to deal with. I have sat with surgeons concerned about the obese people they were operating on, and nurses who had to lift them and turn them in their beds. They told me that, quite apart from the health risks, hospitals were having to buy larger beds, more powerful hoists for the wards and bigger fridges for the mortuary.

And I have listened to primary care professionals and public health staff complaining about the fried chicken shops and fast food outlets that provide much of the diet of their patients, as well as the fizzy drinks and lack of exercise. I have talked with mental health workers struggling to tackle teenage suicides and angry that too many people are stuck in mental health hospitals simply because there isn't suitable housing for them.

Government, of course, can help deal with some of these things. Legislation on smoking and, before that, on seat belts and health and safety at work are of fundamental importance. But we might ask why it took 50 years from the time of the first convincing evidence of the effects of smoking to the introduction of legislation banning it in public places. And government action in recent years on childhood obesity and sugar, for example, has similarly been a long drawn-out process of small movements in the right direction, each one seemingly wrung out of a reluctant government.

Climate change is upon us and so is the global spread of viruses. Both point to the vital role the UK Government has in working with all nations globally to protect the planet and all its citizens. We are interdependent and in the face of pandemics or bioterrorism are only as strong as the weakest link in the chain of surveillance and control.

But what government gives, it can also take away. We have seen this in recent years in the shredding of social infrastructure in the UK and other countries, brought about in the name of austerity. There is compelling evidence that this has harmed health, and it appears to have also damaged the very fabric of society.

The value of the work undertaken by unpaid carers in the UK was estimated in 2015 to be almost exactly the same at £132 billion as the cost of publicly funded health and social care. The value of the wider informal care and community system – embracing the voluntary groups of all kinds that keep communities together, from older peoples' day centres and youth clubs to recreational facilities and libraries – is much higher.

When the informal systems are strong, they take some of the strain off the formal system, but when they are weakened, as they have been over recent years, they throw pressure onto the NHS and social care. This has been happening all around us: cuts in the independent living allowance have made many disabled people more dependent and increased costs overall, just as reductions in grants to voluntary organisations have left more people dependent on the state. This is surely bad politics as well as bad economics.

The effects of austerity and associated changes in the culture of public service delivery mean that it is no surprise that many people no longer feel they live in a society that cares about them. The political climate has done a great deal to destroy trust. The coming together in response to the pandemic may help but, even here, poorer people with fewer resources of all kinds are facing worse problems.

Good health is good for the economy, a healthy workforce is a productive one, and improving health in childhood and old age reduces costs as well as improving quality of life. In recent years, government has invested heavily in health research and health science, supported entrepreneurs and life sciences; but the effects are not yet being felt in the poorer parts of the country.

The UK is a world leader in health and health sciences, respected and influential, and with wise leadership can develop still further to the benefit of the world as well as itself. Its reputation, however, is suffering at the time of writing owing to the high death rate from the virus and the way the Government has handled the pandemic. It is, of course, too early to know how this will play out in the coming months and years.

***

It is in this country of conflicting trends, some very positive and some very negative, that my story unfolds.

The people I have met on my journey are improving the world around them. Alone they are impressive, together they can change the world. There is a movement of people and ideas but it is not yet joined up. We need to turn it into a powerful *Movement*, which can change the whole way we think about health.

And there will be opposition. There are many people with vested interests in the status quo, and many others with conflicting priorities who will raise objections and fight change.

Politics too often presents us with false choices. The two major parties have long stood respectively for the market and for state control. The health creators are recreating the third pillar – community or civil society – and in doing so, they are creating health, putting caring back into society and rebuilding communities. They are in the vanguard of change.

And, in what could be a positive sign, politicians of all parties seem to be beginning to rediscover community and communities.

Health is made at home is also a call to action. In 1948, the UK led the world by setting up the NHS as a comprehensive health service *'free at the point of need'*. It was based on the Beveridge Report and was a great national coming together around the shared purpose of providing health services for everyone. It was part of a wider approach embracing education, housing, social support and much more that led to the establishment of a welfare state.

Today's new approach needs to be equally wide-ranging, recognising that healthy individuals depend on healthy communities, a healthy society and a healthy planet. We also need to learn from today's pioneering health creators, embrace them and their ideas and methods, and treat them as equal partners with the NHS and government. In the words of this book's subtitle, we need to work together in *building a healthy and health-creating society*.

But there is no Beveridge to guide us today as we take on these problems, no blueprint for what we should be doing. Nor should there be.

In today's more democratic age we don't need tablets of stone delivered from on high but a future that is built bottom up.

We need to create the future for ourselves.

***

The first big idea that we can learn from the pioneers is the most obvious but probably the most difficult to do in practice. Put simply, we need to *take off our NHS spectacles and think about health differently*. It is very easy to assume that the way we do things now is the natural way to do them. Or that what worked well in the past will work well in the future. Or that health professionals and the health system always know best.

Health is made at home asks us to think differently about ideas and about people. It shows that we can learn from people living on benefits in a Greater Manchester housing estate or those living in rural Africa. They have a different vantage point on the world and may well have new insights to share.

We all have our own views and values, of course, and many people have strongly held religious and political beliefs. The essential point is that these beliefs shouldn't so restrict our view that we can't understand another way of seeing the world. Or appreciate it or, even better, learn what we can from it.

Nor should any of this go against the great principles of science and objectivity. Science asks questions, is sceptical and encourages us to challenge our own ideas.

We should allow ourselves to think freely and, when it comes to it, act accordingly.

We need to take off our NHS spectacles – and keep them off.

PART TWO

THE HEALTH
CREATORS

CHAPTER THREE

GOOD FOR THE BUSINESS AND THE RIGHT THING TO DO

My journey in the UK starts in the workplace, where we typically spend so much of our time and where our experiences, achievements, stresses and strains shape so much of the rest of our lives. A positive atmosphere with challenging and enjoyable work and supportive colleagues helps us feel good. But it is also a place where disaster can hit any of us, at any time and whatever our background.

Brian Heyworth is a high-flying banking executive who crashed to earth a few years ago when he had a complete mental breakdown and spent the next two months in hospital. It felt like the end of his career, he told me, and probably his whole way of life. Who would employ him after this? How could he make a living? What would he tell his children? How could he face the future?

Yet it was only a few months later that he was being interviewed for a more senior job in a different bank by a hard-bitten executive, who told Brian that he knew his capabilities and wanted him on his team. They spent much of the interview talking about his mental illness and the progress of his rehabilitation. In a remarkable statement, the executive said that at least Brian now knew what his problems were and, more importantly, he was dealing with them. Unlike many of the other people in the business.

They were in an upstairs office that looked out onto a busy trading floor and the executive gestured down at the people below. *'What the hell do you think is going on inside all their heads?'* he asked. *'Look at them!'*

Brian looked. Five floors down there were hundreds of people in the large central space, grouped around screens, talking, walking, or sitting alone with headsets on or an ear pressed to a phone. It was a scene of constant movement, groups forming and reforming, screens flashing around them. He couldn't hear any of the noise but could imagine the overwhelming volume, both human and electronic, which he knew only added to the sense of chaos.

What indeed? What neuroses and psychoses were at play below them? What outward show of success and achievement masked depression, addiction and damaged relationships? At least Brian was tackling his own problems. It was hard but he was getting them under control. It made perfect business sense to employ him.

I'd heard something like this before from a GP in East London who told me that the City workers moving into the area were bringing with them a new range of problems into his surgery. Anxiety, depression, stress and addictions were now becoming common. It seems the masters of the universe can be at their most vulnerable inside their own heads. And Brian's new boss evidently knew it.

But, as Brian explained, it is unusual to spend most of a job interview talking about your mental breakdown and how your rehabilitation is going. You would normally try to avoid the topic.

Meeting with me over a coffee, he spoke candidly about his experiences. Growing up in a privileged environment, well-known public school, Cambridge, banking, married with children, all the trappings of success. But looking back, he could now see the signs of the pressure building up – and the pain. He had anaesthetised himself with alcohol and other substances as he approached the moment when it all imploded.

He spoke comfortably, relaxed, a dry humour concealing any emotion; telling me that before his breakdown he had attended any number of evening events with the bank where, like everyone else, he had to pretend he was sober as the evening wore on. Now that he didn't drink anymore, he had to pretend he was as plastered as everyone else. *Plus ça change*. We laughed.

Brian told me all this for a reason. He had recently become the chair of the City Mental Health Alliance, a group of some of the major companies in the City of London's financial district that had come together to tackle mental health problems among their employees. His candour was important. He and other senior people – city lawyers, bankers, accountants, businesspeople, regulators – were willing to tell their deeply personal stories in order to help others and bring about change in their organisations.

This last point is very important. The overriding aim is not to help employees become more resilient so they can cope with bad practice but to *change* that practice.

It is part of a wider social trend for self-revelation, which now includes royalty, actors, politicians and other well-known figures, who are helping to make it acceptable and easier to talk about mental health. And talking about it without shame is a necessary first step towards dealing with it.

The Alliance doesn't just talk though – its members are actively putting in place training and programmes for their organisations. Their aims are impressive: to increase mental health literacy; give people confidence and the appropriate language to talk about mental illness; create a culture of openness; and help employers take practical steps, giving them the tools and the knowledge to do so.

There's a lot going on. A quick scroll through the Alliance website reveals a City law firm running training for its line managers; a major data and media company working with the mental health charity Mind to improve policies; and the Bank of England promoting resilience training and a peer support network. There are advice and support lines, fact sheets and different levels of counselling available to staff. As I read through the descriptions of what companies are doing, I noticed common themes recurring and important connections being made. This is about health, wellbeing and productivity, about the emotional, financial and physical wellbeing of City employees, and about workplace wellness, not just mental health.

I was struck by a blog written by the Alliance's chief executive called 'Challenging perfectionism', in which she talked about helping young people in their transition into the workplace. She wrote: *'Presenting workplaces as perfect, sleek organisations with no room for flaws does not reflect reality. It is counterproductive for both parties. Flaws and imperfections are the things that make us unique and it is our individuality that brings diversity of thought into the workplace, which every leader knows is critical for business success. Work can be challenging. Working hours can be challenging …'*

One young woman is quoted as saying: *'We have this added pressure throughout education. I can't trip up, I have to be perfect, otherwise I don't have any prospects for the future.'*

These are not just matters for the City, of course, but profound issues about the stresses of modern life, which I was to hear much more about on my journey in all kinds of different environments, from schools to housing estates to hospitals. Here, as elsewhere, the leaders of organisations like the Alliance are confronting problems which, if not checked, lead inexorably on to the GP's surgery and the hospital. Health can be destroyed in the workplace as well as created.

Fifty years ago, the biggest health problems at work were all physical, arising from issues like working with hazardous substances, manual handling, noise and vibration, and operating in dangerous buildings. These issues still exist, of course, but there is now far greater focus on employees' mental health and healthy lifestyles. Today, many employers are not just addressing health problems but actively seeking to promote the health of their employees, through gyms, healthy food, access to advice, cycling facilities and much more. And there is a rapidly growing industry catering to this drive on health in some business sectors.

Now, the biggest and most neglected health issues concern mental health: stress, anxiety, depression and work-life balance and, if we are unlucky, unreasonable workloads, bullying, poor conditions and insecurity. The human costs are immense but so are the financial impacts, with mental illness estimated to cost employers at least £33 billion a year and the UK economy at least £74 billion.

A growing number of employers are starting to address these issues, and relaxation rooms, massage and counselling are appearing in companies all over the world. It would be easy to be cynical about these developments and suggest they have only been set up for commercial reasons because companies need well-functioning employees. It is true that these companies rely on the skills of high-performing individuals, who need to be looked after and kept in peak form. Financial athletes, legal acrobats, deal-making executives. The firms want to maximise the potential of what economists would call their human capital but what the rest of us would refer to as people and their health and wellbeing, their fulfilment, their happiness even.

One of the aims of the Alliance is to work with the media to encourage greater understanding and positive reporting about the City. This is good public relations, of course. But it is also vital for the overall aims of the Alliance because media engagement is a good barometer of the business culture. Creating a culture of openness requires the business to be open to conversation on sensitive subjects at every level. It is about smashing stigma, and inspiring and influencing other organisations and cultures where mental health is still regarded as something to be ignored.

There was more to this, however, than just the interests of the companies involved. It was obvious from listening to Brian that this was also personal. He had been there and his whole world had been shaken by the experience. Other senior leaders also understood on a human level. It is about values as well as adding value. This approach is good for businesses as well as being the right thing to do. It is a point we will return to in Chapter 11, in discussing companies that recognise they have responsibilities to society, their communities and employees, as well as to their shareholders.

I talked more about the Alliance with Poppy Jaman, its chief executive, who I have known for some years as one of the people who brought Mental Health First Aid to England. This is the simple but profound idea that places of employment need trained mental health first aiders, as well as the more familiar first aiders who deal ordinarily with physical problems. Mental first aiders can spot problems developing early and point people to where they can find help. They are good listeners and can also help create a healthy environment. There is as much need for help with stress and depression at work as there is for bandaging fingers and coping with the occasional physical injury – more perhaps.

Poppy has worked for years in mental health but had only relatively recently begun to talk publicly about her own experiences and why she is so passionate about the subject. She told me that one day in 2017 she took a deep breath and started talking unscripted to a conference of City workers. She told them that she was the daughter of migrants from Bangladesh and that her grandfather had worked in Portsmouth Docks, earning a basic living and supporting family back home. Her father was a restaurant owner and worked around the clock. Her mother felt isolated, far from home with limited English language skills, and she developed a number of health issues including depression and anxiety.

Poppy found herself growing up fast. She was supporting her mother, playing an adult role in her brothers' lives, and dealing with everything that arose from banking to housing and even the police. Money was tight and she knew the stigma of not having the right uniform as well as being one of very few Muslim girls at her school.

Poppy said she was torn between cultures at the time and that there were, as she put it, *'two or three versions of me'*. She was both head girl, nominated by a teacher who recognised her potential, and at the same time very rebellious, running away to London with a boyfriend. She took with her only some photos of her family, her GCSE results and £10.30 for her train fare to Waterloo. Back home within ten days, she was whisked straight away to Bangladesh, where she was kept isolated in the family home for almost a year, becoming deeply religious and eventually accepting marriage to an older man.

Returning to England, now with a husband and small baby, she suffered acutely from postnatal depression and retreated into her religion and spirituality. Her health visitor helped her, she said, but the various therapists who saw her simply didn't understand the cultural nuances, and Poppy found herself trying to educate them as well as heal herself. Her work was a lifeline too. An opportunity came when her line manager, another person who had spotted her talent, sent her on an NHS leadership programme for people from black and minority ethnic communities.

It was a revelation. Particularly the modules on oppression and visioning. She felt empowered by the understanding she gained and freed by the ability to visualise a different future for herself. The visioning was extraordinary in itself, she said, for someone who previously hadn't been allowed to travel beyond the end of the street alone. New jobs, divorce, a new marriage all followed, and now she is a visionary chief executive of a pioneering organisation. There is much more to her story than these brief paragraphs can convey and I hope that someday Poppy will write it herself. It is, as she said, a journey of self-discovery and of wanting to be a single human being – a single version of herself.

I can only imagine how the conference audience reacted as they heard this poised and articulate woman tell her story. Poppy told me she was struck by the strength and particularly the warmth of their response. *'I always thought you were from Oxbridge,'* someone told her afterwards, *'probably from a wealthy Asian family.'*

These are stories we normally keep private or only share with close friends or family, and even then, probably only when we have no other option. Poppy and Brian, of course, were using theirs for a purpose: to create debate, open up culture and make change. This is the single most important starting point in addressing mental health at work – or anywhere else.

Her story helps explain why Poppy is so passionate about mental health but not what she was doing here among the big names of the City of London. She had worked for government and NGOs but what she saw here was the opportunity to work with these global brands to change how society sees mental health. These companies have enormous networks and huge influence. They could help bring about change in attitudes to mental health way beyond their own smart offices and dealing rooms. Corporate social responsibility, Poppy told me, is too often random; this was that rare alignment of good for the organisations, good for their staff and good for wider society.

The profile and status of the City firms have helped ensure that they have been able to draw on the best health advice available, partly from the NHS but also from leading NGOs. Both Mental Health First Aid England and Mind are partners and provide expertise and support. This means that the Alliance is led by business and guided by experts, and professional in both aspects.

Paul Farmer, chief executive of Mind, has been an adviser from the early days of the Alliance. He has also written with Lord Dennis Stevenson a report for the Government, *Thriving at Work*, which identifies the evidence and sets six standards for employers to achieve in order to improve the mental health of their employees.

Their report shows that 300,000 people with a long term mental health problem lose their jobs each year and that 15 per cent of the workforce at any time have symptoms of an existing mental health condition. The report's analysis also shows that the cost to employers of this is between £33 billion and £42 billion, and the cost to the economy as a whole is between £74 billion and £99 billion a year. Moreover, evaluations of workplace interventions show a return to business of between £1.50 and £9 for every £1 invested.

These figures are very broad brush but they show that mental health is undoubtedly a big issue for businesses, whether they perceive it as such or not. Happily, there is now a national blueprint for progress, which will help any employer plan its actions.

Paul is very positive about the Alliance, stressing the importance of it being business led and *'a coalition of the willing'*. It is also very realistic in its aims, he told me, making progress step by step, and it had come a long way in a few years. His only word of caution was that it isn't yet possible to measure its impact properly. He stressed the word *yet* because it is still early days for the whole area of workforce health.

Looking more broadly, there has been very good progress in organisations implementing the report's six standards and Paul pointed me to Mind's Workplace Wellbeing Index, which provides a benchmark for best policy and practice. But we are still in the foothills, he told me, with much more to come in future years.

Looking forward in the City of London, Poppy Jaman's ambitions for the Alliance are not just national but global, reflecting the international nature of the City's workforce. The City Mental Health Alliance Hong Kong was launched in late 2017 with several of the City of London members involved, as well as others. It operates on a type of franchise model, working within the aims of the Alliance but focusing on local issues and local people. There are plans for other countries too. The next will be Australia, with Sweden, Singapore and New Zealand all expressing interest.

Representatives of the Swedish Government had asked Poppy to set up an Alliance in Sweden without apparently recognising that this had to be business led. It needed influential senior champions who believed in it, understood its purpose and would own the whole project. Governments can't start up an alliance like Poppy's organisation or make it national policy, but they can convene meetings, signal support and, where necessary, flatter the egos of company leaders into doing something themselves. And they can also adopt the policies outlined in *Thriving at Work* to support their own employees.

The Alliance has come a long way since it was founded in late 2012 by Nigel Jones, at the time a partner in one of the big London law firms, and two colleagues, Pete Rodgers and Paddy Watt, from an accountancy firm and a bank, respectively. I met Nigel around that time when they were planning the way forward. They were motivated by what they had seen and experienced – both positive and negative in their own workplaces – but they needed to persuade others. I attended some of their meetings and heard people from different City organisations talking about the issues and sharing their ideas about how to make the business case. The details were different in each organisation but there was undoubtedly strength to be drawn from the sharing and collaboration. It was already becoming an embryo movement for change across the City.

Nigel's own interest in health went back to his teens when he had wanted to be a doctor rather than a lawyer. He pursued that interest shortly after becoming a partner in 1995 by creating his firm's first sector-focused group, covering the healthcare sector, and later becoming his firm's first health and wellbeing champion. His firm, like others, had a gym and a staff assistance scheme, but its approach to health was far from comprehensive and lacked senior leadership. He was also very conscious that the firm, again like many others in the City, had a culture of long hours and work practices that he knew were, in the long term, detrimental to the quality of its client services, the profitability of the firm and the health of employees alike.

Nigel questioned why the firm engaged in practices that partners knew to be counterproductive. The answer he was given was that their clients – including banks and accountancy firms – demanded short deadlines and created the pressure. It was at a meeting with two clients, who said they had exactly the same issues, that Nigel, Pete and Paddy took the first steps towards setting up the Alliance. That collaboration was vital, Nigel told me. It gave them the strength to do something. They weren't just, as he put it, isolated wimps, but a strong group of people working together on key business issues.

They had gone together to see their three CEOs or chairs and obtained their support and a small amount of funding. They were ready to launch the Alliance when the bank, which had previously signed up to it, suddenly announced that its name could not be used. It wasn't willing to be the only bank associated with something that had mental health in its title, thereby both revealing the stigma associated with the whole topic and showing how radical the approach was at the time. They had to regroup and plan again.

A few months later, they launched the Alliance with ten members including three banks, again showing the advantages of collaboration. There was safety in numbers. And all 110 people who had signed up for the launch actually attended the event – a very rare occurrence to have no one dropping out and a sign in itself of how the initiative served an important need.

Seven years on from the launch, I spoke to Nigel again. He told me that collaboration has continued to be a very strong theme for the Alliance and, with it, the creation of a safe space where people can tell their stories, admit their weaknesses and vulnerabilities, and share experiences on practical measures that could help. He made the very telling point that people should not be afraid to be themselves. *'Acting for most of us is hard work,'* he said. *'Pretending to be someone else means you have to remember your lines. Just being yourself is much easier.'*

The quest for a business case has also moved on with less emphasis on numbers, except where a specific investment is needed, and a more general awareness that investing in the mental wellbeing of their people is simply the right thing for firms to be doing – against whatever criterion that is assessed. Nigel and the other founders have also achieved the difficult feat of passing leadership onto the next generation, increasing the chances of the Alliance remaining sustainable into the future.

None of the organisations in the Alliance would claim to have got it all right yet; there is still a long way to go and there remains some resistance. Culture takes time to change and this purposeful approach to health and wellbeing hasn't yet found its place alongside other organisational strategies in all businesses. But culture is clearly changing, and I would suggest that in the seven years of its existence, the Alliance has helped employee health and wellbeing move from being seen as a 'nice to have' add-on to being a genuine business priority.

The City Mental Health Alliance is only one of many examples, nationally and globally, where employers are taking action to address the health and wellbeing of their workers, and the Farmer/Stevenson report has undoubtedly given extra momentum to this growing movement. Among others, the NHS in England is setting an example, working to improve the health of its 1.4 million-strong workforce, championed by its chief executive. Twitter, too, was alive with nurses talking about exercise – until Covid-19 took over as the main topic for discussion.

There is a great deal to celebrate. Paul Farmer and Mind deserve a lot of credit for building on the movement on workplace mental health in 2010 with their campaign *The Elephant in the Room*, and for already having made such an impact. However, only a minority of the workforce is so far covered in this way. Some sectors are fairly well covered, Paul told me, notably construction and those reliant on the intellectual skills of their workforce, such as those in the City, but others including hospitality have made little progress.

Studies of bullying and abuse in the workplace show these are still significant problems, and redundancies, change and transformation programmes can be handled very badly for the staff involved. Away from the City, at the other end of the scale, there are millions of low-paid workers on zero hours contracts and in the gig economy whose organisations take little or no responsibility for their welfare. Very many workers are in a weaker position on bargaining and rights than they have been for years. These are issues where government undoubtedly needs to take the lead and bring in legislation as necessary.

Automation and robotics have brought about radical changes in many people's working lives and, with the development of artificial intelligence (AI) and new technologies, are set to continue to transform many sectors, bringing with them greater opportunity for some and increased stress and uncertainty for others.

It is easy to understand how for all too many people the uncertainty of their situation turns into real insecurity and mental distress. The famous Whitehall studies of the 1960s, 70s and 80s looked at the mortality and health of civil servants and demonstrated that there was a relationship between their grades of employment and mortality rates from a range of different causes. The lower the grade, the higher the mortality rate. Men in the lowest grade, for example, had a mortality rate three times higher than that of men in the highest grade. It was a counterintuitive finding because the common assumption at the time was that the bosses were the ones who suffered with stress and had the greater risk of heart attacks.

The existence of this *social gradient* across the whole of society, whereby social status is associated with mortality and morbidity, is now well accepted but the reasons for it and how to tackle it are still not understood. In this century, the Whitehall II study is following a new cohort of 10,000 civil servants, and trying to identify the causal pathways and establish the nature of the links between social position, physiological changes, subclinical markers of disease, functional change, and clinical disease.

What is happening in the workplace is influenced by wider society and social trends, some negative and some positive. Austerity and the growth of the contractual society, where obligations and responsibilities are based purely on contracts rather than relationships, are pushing people apart and destroying communities. In this sort of environment, employees are disposable, people are expendable.

The Covid-19 pandemic has raised anxiety levels throughout the population with concerns about health, livelihoods and businesses. Self-isolation is creating extra stress. Millions of people are affected and the impact will be felt for years to come.

But the pandemic has also revealed, in very dramatic terms, the importance to us all of the work done by some of the lowest-paid people in the country, who also have the least security of employment and associated benefits. Supermarket workers, delivery drivers, refuse collectors, postmen and women, farm labourers and many more have played vital roles. Above all, perhaps, the care workers who are often on zero hours contracts. This must surely provide the impetus for improvement in the future.

What is going on in our personal lives also impacts on our work. The stresses, strains and problems of life affect our capabilities, commitment and concentration at work. As the population ages, for example, we can expect more and more employees to have caring responsibilities at home, and this will bring both occasional crises and regular demands on their time and emotions. Some employers are already starting to introduce schemes to support them.

Different generations want and expect different things from the workplace. Paul Farmer told me there is a trend for young people to ask about employers' mental health policies during the recruitment process, thereby putting pressure on organisations to improve on this issue.

Many young people are rejecting employment altogether and setting up their own enterprises, with some interesting examples in later chapters of this book. So too, for that matter, are many older people, never happier than when striking out on their own to pursue latter-day portfolio careers. People want control, autonomy, meaning and the ability to build their own relationships with others. These characteristics feature strongly in later chapters and are associated with health and wellbeing.

The push for diversity is also of central importance: gender, race, disability, sexuality all play their part, positively or negatively in the workplace. As a woman and coming from a Bangladesh background, Poppy Jaman talked about how her mental health problems had manifested, and how different insecurities and tensions had built up inside her. And how they weren't understood.

There is evidence that being significantly different from the majority population, for example, being black in a white society, brings added stress. This is marked, as we now know, by increased levels of cortisol in the body and is associated with increased morbidity and reduced life expectancy. These are issues we will also return to later.

The main point of this chapter, however, is the importance of the workplace to our life, health and wellbeing. We spend long hours at work and bring its issues home to impact on our families and friends, for good or ill. If we are fortunate, work enriches our lives; if not, it can lead us to the GP's surgery and, beyond that, the hospital.

The focus of this chapter has so far been on the employers, the organisations themselves, and their businesses and responsibilities. But individuals play vital roles in any workplace, whether they are senior people, the leaders who make the big decisions, or the informal leaders and networkers who help shape the culture. Brian Heyworth gives enormous credit to the man who recruited him shortly after his breakdown. Poppy Jaman, too, talks warmly of the people who spotted her potential, the teacher and the manager who sent her on that all important course, and the leader of the course itself. Neither of them needed to tell their own stories so publicly but, by doing so, they have influenced many other people. And Nigel Jones and his two colleagues didn't need to set up the City Mental Health Alliance, spend the time developing it, and take the risks with their own reputations in doing so.

Everyone has a part to play in improving health and wellbeing in their workplace, whether it is by taking a leading role or not. They can review their own working practices and those of colleagues. They can persuade their bosses and their employer that it is in the organisation's interests to safeguard and protect the physical and mental health of their employees.

They can notice others in distress, however well they try to hide it, and offer help. And by taking the initiative, empowering themselves, they can take back some control and improve their own mental and physical health – unlike those civil servants of the 1960s and 70s.

The health professions and the NHS have played an important part in supporting the Alliance with the expertise it needs to operate effectively. However, Nigel told me that some psychiatrists are uneasy about all this activity and very concerned that it will just raise demand for mental health services. '*Where would all the extra psychiatrists come from?*' they have asked.

But, as Nigel pointed out, the Alliance's work is more about changing harmful practices, managing stress and preventing illness than about seeking treatment.

'*Yes, prevention, a good idea,*' a very senior psychiatrist told him. '*If only we had the time.*'

These comments reveal a health system under enormous stress, fearful of having to do more. But they also surely expose a deep seated belief within the profession, and no doubt in society at large, that anything to do with health is the NHS's responsibility. Nigel could have replied that we need more good employers rather than more psychiatrists. The comments also reveal that prevention is not just a secondary activity for many in the NHS but is barely on the agenda at all.

It's not just that the NHS can't do everything by itself but why should we even expect it to? The health and wellbeing of employees are surely very much part of any employer's core responsibilities.

The Farmer/Stevenson report, *Thriving at Work*, has set out the evidence and provided a blueprint for action. Change and improvement will take time and effort, and it will require ownership and commitment from senior leaders. It always does. But, as the Alliance has shown, progress can be made with vision, creativity and determination. And it is now time to act.

***

This first stage of my journey has already brought out features and themes that will reappear throughout the book. The importance of truth-telling, for example, as well as communication, connecting with others, and taking control of a problem and owning it. The need for professional help and advice at the right time and on your terms. And the importance of aligning different interests. Here, they are the interests of the employee and the employer – making sure it's good for the business and the right thing to do.

Perhaps the most important theme here, however, is the simple point that anyone can take the first step. Mental health is at last being recognised as of fundamental importance to our overall health and wellbeing. Almost every story I recount in this book has a mental health component. It underpins almost everything else.

The second big idea for taking back control of our health and our communities is *talk about mental health.*

Anyone can do it: employees, staff organisations or employers. Start talking about feelings and mental wellbeing and stress, whatever is the issue in your organisation. But start the conversation, don't wait for others. Take control.

It's time for employers to act – to take responsibility for the health and wellbeing of their employees and see the business benefit from doing so. It's time for employees and their representatives to act – to challenge and hold employers to account, but also to adopt healthy work practices themselves and support their colleagues where necessary.

And it's time for government to act – to enable and incentivise change. But it must also confront the problems of the zero hours and gig economy, which can damage the health of individuals and, in the longer run, the health of society as a whole. Our experience of the valuable work done by so many of the lowest-paid and least secure people during the Covid-19 pandemic must surely add weight to the argument for change.

The first policy change for government in this book is to *review the impact of the zero hours and gig economy on health and wellbeing, and introduce new measures to support and improve the mental and physical health of the workers involved.*

CHAPTER FOUR

EXCLUSION, ASPIRATIONS AND ACHIEVEMENT

This chapter takes us from some of the most affluent people in the land, in the City of London, to some of the poorest and most disadvantaged 50 miles west, in the Thames Valley. Thousands of children in the UK are excluded from school every year, a few thousand of them permanently. Troublesome, disruptive, damaged and even violent children whom teachers struggle to cope with in a normal school environment. That's how we usually describe them anyway. But what if we saw them differently? If we could also see their potential?

I visited two alternative providers that work with excluded children. They operate at the extremes of the education system and see the really difficult health and social issues. Their perspectives offer an insight into the whole system that has rejected and ejected these children.

I was reminded that Lord John Bird, founder of *The Big Issue*, had told me that a million pounds of public money had been spent on most of the people who sold the street newspaper; and some would have had many millions spent on them. They may have been in care as children, in prison, claiming benefit, or in hospital with physical or mental illnesses – each of them 'homeless millionaires'. It costs much less to educate a City banker. And the children I was meeting were more likely to be future

Big Issue sellers, I guessed, than to be dealing in derivatives or working in corporate finance.

***

Mark kitted me out with wellingtons. It had rained overnight and there were fresh puddles in the farm track as we walked down past a barn and on to an open field. An area on the left was given over to vegetable growing with early courgettes and broad beans already beginning to crop. An open fronted wooden building on the right provided space for activities to take place under cover and a large grassed space straight ahead was ringed by half a dozen yurts.

We were less than three miles from Reading, yet it felt as though we were deep in the country. Mark Hillyer had set up Path Hill Farm Outdoor Centre ten years ago as a place where he and his colleagues could work one to one with children who had been permanently excluded from normal schools because of their behaviour.

We talked as we walked. He explained that he had worked for years in environmental education and had seen first-hand how much outdoor activities could help young people with troubled lives. The natural environment, as all the evidence now shows, has a calming effect on the mind and body. And working outdoors, Mark told me, he could always find something that a child was capable of doing and that, for once in their life at least, they could show to themselves and the world what a success they were.

There was so much they could do here, Mark said: putting up a tent, planting vegetables, cooking a meal, or maybe mending a fence or building a structure in the wood. There were only seven children at the centre that day, each doing something different and each with an adult giving them their whole attention. One child was kayaking and another was out buying food for the midday meal. Everyone ate together and the children took turns at cooking with the help of their adult companion. It was the one regular point in the day when everyone came together.

We continued into the wood, which surrounded the field on two sides. Here, Mark showed me another wooden building that they had constructed for group activities. There was a space for a fire and a cooking area. Further along one of the woodland paths we found six year old Dean, who was learning how to make fire. Proudly, he showed me how to do it using a bow and two pieces of wood. It worked first time and he was elated. I was impressed.

It was at moments like this, Mark told me, when they were doing something together, that a child might start talking, asking questions, perhaps even telling the adult what they were worrying about. These conversations were incredibly valuable, Mark explained, since relationships developed as the child opened up and healing could at last begin.

I was wearing a suit and would shortly be on my way to London. But standing there in my borrowed wellingtons I wanted to stay and make fire with Dean. Looking out across the wood, I noticed how it was already transforming from the fresh foliage of spring into the lush and deeper greens of summer, silent and peaceful. I could sense what Mark meant.

It was June 2019. Did I really have to travel down to Parliament and all the anguish and division of Brexit?

There is something here that most of us take for granted: loving adults who value us, time and space to explore and make things, freedom from any worries about the future. A childhood in other words. These children, however, need to learn to trust adults, to regress if necessary to earlier stages of childhood, and to vent some of those emotions they bottle up inside.

I asked about the children, where they came from and why they were here. Neglect featured high on the list of reasons, accompanied sometimes by abuse, addictions, violence and bullying. Many of the children were or had been fostered or were in care. These were children who had experienced the worst start in life and had reacted in whatever way they could to the insults and injuries thrust upon them. They needed to recover. It was intensive care really.

The truth is that these are the children whom most of us never talk to; alien and perhaps threatening figures at the margins of our busy lives. All these children, some as young as Dean and some in their late teens, had already been permanently excluded from school and in a sense from wider society too. Path Hill is registered as an approved provider by the local education authority and takes children for part of the week, perhaps two or three days at a time, while the other days are spent at another provider that offers more formal education.

Path Hill can take 30 children and on the day I visited there were 29 on the roll, all attending part time. Each of them an individual, each with their own history and their own skills and aptitudes. Each child has an Education, Health and Care (EHC) Plan, which sets out the child's interests and aspirations, as well as their needs and how they will be met. The EHC Plan is a legal document designed to bring together the resources of the education, health and social care authorities around the child. It's a great concept. I wondered how well it worked in practice.

Mark has a team from a range of different backgrounds who between them seek to meet the needs of each child. There is no one model of approach, no one profession dominating, but a team of people bringing together practical skills in gardening and carpentry with education, youth work and psychology. Mark tends not to use technical language or jargon but, underneath the commonsense approach, I was aware of the knowledge and thought that goes into the design of programmes for each child. These are children, many with attachment issues, who feel unworthy and inadequate. Some have severe mental disorders, and all need professional help. Mark describes Path Hill in simple terms as a very therapeutic place that uses psychologically informed therapy.

The whole place is geared towards achievement. These are children who have too often been told they are failures, with a concentration on what they can't do, their deficits and problems. Here they find things they can do, minor successes perhaps and small steps forward, striking a flame from bare wood, but it's all part of healing and rehabilitation.

I asked Mark how they measure their success. The short answer is individually. It all depends on what happens with each individual and whether they can find the right next steps for them. For most of the children, this is being absorbed back into the school system, probably at a special school. But Mark mentioned one young man who was being tutored at home. More broadly, he talks about the importance of managing transitions more effectively – into schools, into or out of care perhaps, out of education and into adulthood. There aren't any easy answers here; recovery and rehabilitation aren't a linear process.

I asked about how Mark sees the future for approved providers. He told me about the need for outreach. He doesn't want children excluded from school and sent to Path Hill but believes that more of them could be supported to stay where they are. He also thinks that he and his colleagues could help teachers to keep more children in school. They could intervene earlier and try to pre-empt admission to the 'intensive care' of Path Hill.

Mark is passionate about the value of outdoor education and feels young teachers now are too computer bound and too constrained by assessment tests and inspections to provide a rounded education. He welcomes schools and other groups to Path Hill; some camping overnight in the yurts and some using the other facilities. And he wants more centres like Path Hill where children can learn in different ways and get closer to nature.

In some ways he's quite optimistic, he said. Welcoming the new emphasis on the environment and sustainability, he also sees greater acceptance of difference and diversity in society. It's not all 'one size fits all' anymore. But there are funding problems and a need to intervene earlier in children's lives, a more preventive approach that will reduce the stream of damaged children coming to Path Hill.

What happens to these children now will help shape their future health, physically and mentally. Some of it is already determined of course – made in the home – but intervening now can still make a difference. I wonder how many of these children will be *The Big Issue* sellers of the future with their million pound histories, or whether we will learn to intervene earlier and more decisively. What does the future hold for six year old Dean?

***

A few days later and I am back in Reading to visit Mandy Wilton, the head of another approved provider, Cranbury College in Reading. The College is much bigger than Park Hill with 132 places for children spread over four sites. It is housed in old school buildings, run down and in need of repair, and which don't give the impression that the local authority is proud of the place.

These were difficult kids, Mandy told me; children with mental illnesses, 14 year olds involved in county lines drug running, some of them just running wild. One of her jobs, she said, is to try to keep them coming to the College, not scare them off, and engage them in positive activities. But she is not always successful.

'*What happens then?*' I asked.

'*Well sometimes they just disappear,*' she replied.

It was a bleak picture of 21st century Britain. These were, she said, children who were not needed by anyone and could too easily be influenced, put into an environment where other kids taught them the really bad stuff. They didn't have a childhood, she said. And their futures as adults didn't look good either.

Mandy said when she was appointed, a district councillor had told her: '*This place is a dustbin you know, where we put all our problems. We only worry when the lid wobbles.*'

It was all very depressing.

'*So what do you do?*' I asked.

The answer unsurprisingly was very like Mark's: '*We work with aspirations.*'

Cranbury College is a school and therefore has greater emphasis on formal education. Indeed, Mandy stresses the importance of reading, writing and maths, and the skills that enable you to function in society. But she and her staff are also able to work with individuals on the things they want to do – carpentry perhaps, or cooking or art. Their main focus is on aspiration and success and praising the children wherever they can.

They have a relationship policy, she explained, not a behavioural one. It's not about school rules but about relating to each other. There are boundaries, of course, but you don't need to spell them out if the key thing is learning to relate to other people. It takes time and perseverance and, as adults, she and her colleagues have to absorb the insults when the students first arrive and try to refocus. She told me about one young man whom she greets in a friendly fashion every morning; but it was only after several weeks of this that he became willing to acknowledge her and respond. It's a start. Something to build on.

We talked about the links between health and education, and how children have to be ready and able to learn, which means you have to deal with their basic needs first. Sometimes it's as simple as providing them with breakfast, as the College does every day. And there are all the health issues to do with sex, drugs, healthy lifestyles, nutrition. Girls' sport is important, Mandy said. And then, of course, there is mental health and, she added, healthy sleep.

The first five years of life are very important for health but so too is adolescence. It is a vulnerable time. The brain and the body are still developing and, as a result, young people have particular health needs. And, of course, puberty frequently brings angst and a loss of confidence, together with greater self-consciousness about our bodies, sexuality, gender and relationships. Our parents if we have them, our communities, our teachers, social media and, above all, our peer group influence us profoundly – helping create our health at home, in the community, at school or, as here, in the care of Mandy and her colleagues.

Ofsted rates Cranbury College as good but, ultimately, success for Mandy is about what happens when the children leave and about them being able to contribute positively to society. And that takes her back to nurturing their aspirations. She has one young man who wants to be a carpenter and the College has organised ways to support him, helping him to learn and perhaps go on to do an apprenticeship. A young girl wants to be a midwife but this is going to be much harder with many more hurdles to overcome; particularly, Mandy said, when starting from where she is now.

And Mandy agrees with Mark about the need for outreach and that too many children are excluded. More than half a million children in the UK are temporarily excluded from school each year and about 20,000 are permanently excluded.

More children should stay in mainstream schools but the local context is very difficult. The children's services department has been classified as inadequate and there are two very poor special schools. There are such low aspirations for these kids. But Mandy told me there is a fightback going on. Organisations across Reading are trying to work together across boundaries – health with education and social services, and housing and the police – developing communities and *'joining the dots'*.

And there are successes. Mandy told me how she met a former pupil in the street recently. *'Hey Miss,'* the young woman called out proudly, *'I'm a taxpayer now.'*

Maybe she will soon be joined by a midwife and a carpenter.

***

Back in London, Dorcas Gwata, an NHS clinical nurse specialist who was originally from Zimbabwe, reinforced for me some of the things I had learned in Reading. She was running a programme in the Borough of Westminster, part research and part practical action, which was designed to promote the mental health of young gang members affected by knife crime and exploitation, 90 per cent of whom were black African or Caribbean.

There was, she told me, an enormous gap between how services were designed and the reality of the young peoples' lives. There were some basic but hidden problems that many of us wouldn't think about, such as how to reach a 14 year old who couldn't cross a postcode boundary to get to a clinic. And problems, too, in how risk assessments were done. The professionals needed to understand the environment and, for example, to know who in the neighbourhood was running drugs and who would shortly be coming out of prison.

Everything was massively complicated by the different cultures and backgrounds of the young people, themselves a part of the rich diversity of the city. And, of course, it was made worse by racism, inequalities, crime and poverty.

Dorcas is a mental health nurse but was working across the three agencies of health, social services and education. She was able to draw on her own experience of working in Africa to address some of the cultural issues in the training sessions she ran for parents and professionals to help them recognise the early signs of mental illness. She told me that her research on the Zimbabwean Bench Project, an HIV mental health programme, gave her a culturally appropriate way of engaging young people, which proved useful in working with young people exposed to violence in Westminster. She also pointed out that this showed that low income countries have lessons to teach. And her research showed how important this sort of multi-agency working is in providing a holistic view of a situation and being able to tackle some of these multi-faceted problems.

Talking with Dorcas opened up another world, another part of the UK. But it was what she said at the end of our conversation that was most striking. She spoke about the difficulty in reaching young people in chaotic and unstable homes. *'But the biggest risk,'* she said, *'was in exclusion from school. They exclude young vulnerable children too easily in Westminster.'* And she told me that the student referral units in the borough were a breeding ground for gangs, stirring up mental health problems, addictions and all sorts of risky behaviours. It echoed Mandy Wilton's and Mark Hillyer's comments.

Not only do we throw these young people out for bad behaviour but we send them to places where they can learn even worse habits. Where was their childhood, the adult attention, the praise, the successes and the aspirations for better lives?

Exclusion, special schools and their approach to children with these sorts of serious difficulties are one area where the public authorities are getting things hopelessly wrong. Government needs to listen and learn from these examples. It needs to invest millions upfront on prevention and development instead of spending even greater sums later in life on some of these young people. It would be cheaper and better to do so now.

It's not just education that's the issue here. Youth services and other local authority provision have been cut back through years of austerity, but these and later examples in *Health is made at home* show what can be done by anyone – police officers, parents and young people themselves – to improve life for young people and the community. It can't just be left to the authorities.

And one of the strengths of a community is its young people. We exclude them from school or anywhere else at our peril.

***

Professor John Ashton is a distinguished and innovative former public health director for the North West of England. He led the way in many areas, from promoting needle exchanges for addicts to seeking to influence patterns of crime and behaviour in young people. He emailed me an article in the *Liverpool Echo* describing how an official from Cali in Colombia, Dr Alberto Concha-Eastman, was working with him to advise the city on tackling knife crime.

Local Police Superintendent Mark Wiggins had already told a meeting of representatives from the police, health, education and local authority sectors that austerity driven cutbacks to youth work had *'undoubtedly'* led to a rise in knife crime. Dr Concha-Eastman followed on by telling the group that the formative years of a child's life are key to preventing criminal and violent activity and described love as essential.

He told them: *'In 1996, I conducted research in my city to interview 50 (murderers) in prison and compare their lifetime with another 50 men from the same neighbourhood where the inmates used to live when they were out.*

'The difference in their life stories was totally amazing. Those in prison, those murderers, they didn't have a guidance in their early lives. They didn't receive true love.

'They didn't trust anybody, overwhelmingly the father was absent. Those who never committed a homicide, or never committed an assault or crime, they received love, received guidance, in schooling and family.'

Interesting as the article was, it was the published responses from some of the readers to the online version that stayed with me. There were comments about *'Bleeding hearts'* and *'If you want to do a good turn for them smack heads, put them asleep for good'*, before the conversation declined into a set of political arguments about austerity, Tony Blair, socialism and the history of Liverpool.

It reminded me that not everyone sees things in the same way and that there would be some public and political opposition to the ideas expressed so clearly by Mark Hillyer and Mandy Wilton, as well as to the notion that we must invest in these children – with money and love.

***

This chapter introduces another of the big ideas that can make all the difference. Like the others it is deceptively simple. It is *focus on relationships*.

This works at the personal level: a parent's love or the personal connection that Mark Hillyer and colleagues are trying to make with their charges – trusting, confiding, nurturing relationships that affect lives forever.

It works for the professional case worker who, as Dorcas Gwata explained, has to find ways to listen to and understand the world of the young people they are working with, and to learn how to build a relationship with them.

It also works at the organisational level with Mandy Wilton and Cranbury College's relationship policy, rather than a behavioural approach. There are boundaries, of course, but the emphasis is on relating to others.

And, as we will see later, it is vital in the workplace, in businesses and in shared endeavours of every sort where personal relationships, trust and shared interests determine what you can get done – and not, as we normally assume, systems, structures and lines of authority. These things matter, of course, but it is the strength of the person to person relationships that makes things happen.

This chapter has also pointed to the failure of government policies on exclusion from school, and special schools. The way they are currently designed seems almost to guarantee that these children will be excluded for life, always be on the outside, just collateral damage in the campaign to improve our schools.

These failures have profound long term effects not least on our health system, where we will be paying the price for years to come.

The NHS will be doing the repairs but it is powerless to deal with the underlying causes.

The second big policy action for government is to *review and reform policy and practice on exclusion from school and implement changes as a priority.*

CHAPTER FIVE

THE PRESSURE TO BE PERFECT

It's easy to turn our backs on people if they don't fit in. And to underestimate them.

Shanna Dawes was saying that people thought that growing up in Cornwall must be idyllic but it wasn't like that really, not in a town like Camborne with its big council estates and nothing much else. It was easy to fall in with the wrong crowd. At the age of 13 her normal Friday night out consisted of going into town with her friends and getting drunk.

Not anymore. The first time Shanna attended a new dance workshop in Camborne in 2004, she nearly went straight home again because there were so many police officers there. But the music drew her in and she stayed, along with 100 others. And she discovered that the police were human too.

I watched Shanna's TED talk on my phone as I travelled down by train almost to the farthest tip of Cornwall. I was on my way to see the dance school for myself and meet some of the people involved. Sergeant David Aynsley was the policeman who had been in charge that night in 2004 and, like Shanna, he had been frustrated by the lack of anything to do in the town and was thoroughly fed up with spending his time arresting children for minor crimes and reporting them for truanting.

Today, more than 15 years later, the dance school is an established part of Camborne life with more than 2000 young people, aged five to 18, having been members at some time during those years. Shanna is now an international dance teacher and David, while no longer in the police, is still deeply involved in the dance school, which is now run by the young people themselves. Research by the University of Exeter is beginning to reveal very positive health and other benefits for these young people.

Following a chance encounter with Hazel Stuteley, a former nurse, David and his team undertook the C2 Connecting Communities programme. This resulted in them starting to lead street games with the children and listening to what they wanted. It was a change from chasing and cautioning them, and immediately more productive. Another chance meeting, this time with a professional dancer and choreographer who just happened to be staying in the town, led to the launch of dance classes. On the first night, 120 young people turned up at the hall and things began to change.

It wasn't all easy, of course. Forming a charity, which quickly attracted substantive funding, led to internal power struggles between adult board members, including one very traumatic case of fraud. However, the group adapted and responded quickly by reframing its governance so that the majority of trustees and directorships are held by young dance leaders over the age of 16. Over the years, the group have raised in excess of £10,000 to support themselves through sheer hard work including supermarket bag packing, cake stalls, sponsored walks and shows. Current charitable sponsors include Children in Need and Awards for All.

Since the 2008-09 recession, however, it has been a financial struggle to sustain and develop the activities, and they haven't yet been able to realise their dream of having their own dance hall, receiving little or no support from local authorities. Remarkably, every workshop since the group launched has been free to attend. This will never change.

At a personal level, David was criticised in the local paper and by his superiors for what he was doing and was told to go back to traditional policing. *'This* is *traditional policing,'* he protested. *'My grandfather used to play football with the local youths as a policeman in Surrey.'*

I watched a young woman, Tia Fannelli, lead a class of 25 young people through a new dance routine with great confidence and flair. She had just become the youngest company director, joining the board at 16. Shanna had said in her TED talk that '*all we as young people wanted was stability and a chance to be listened to*'. I could see some of the results for myself.

One of the most interesting things was how leadership worked in the group. Anyone could step forward to be a leader and ask for one of the tee shirts that had 'leader' written across the back. Tia had one and there were several others in her class including, I noticed, a young woman with Down's syndrome who was absorbed in her dance. It was a system that appeared to work. Everyone knew, of course, who the stars were, the role models who the younger ones wanted to emulate. But you didn't need to be a star to be a leader. And being a leader wasn't about bossing people around but about confidence and being willing to stand up in public to do something. Take a lead. Start a dance.

I also met Becci Gowers, a professionally trained dance teacher, who had nurtured this leadership style and supported the group for many years. She, together with former dance leaders Sean and Alex, coach the young leaders to choreograph their own routines. They then teach them to younger members, some as young as five.

These were not by any means excluded children, or unwanted. These were children we might meet anywhere in the UK: funny, bright, endlessly inventive, testing the boundaries and not content to be told what to do. They were having fun. There was a family atmosphere in the church hall where the classes were held, with the young people looking out for each other and some of the mothers coming to the class too, even joining in. I talked to some of the young people who told me the class was the highlight of their week. And they asked me if I knew Alan Sugar, Boris Johnson and the Queen. In that order. And I was told to say that '*Jill says Hi*' if I ever met any of them.

Camborne is officially described as a deprived area, although David and Hazel don't want to talk about deprivation or use other labels like 'vulnerable children'. They prefer to talk about promoting social rights and the ability of young people to be fully part of society, take opportunities and, of course, contribute. It's a point David made, albeit in a different way, when he said he was head of a police antisocial behaviour unit but had never heard of a police *social* behaviour unit. The latter could perhaps help to build relationships, community and aspiration.

The young people named the dance workshops the TR14ers after the postcode, because of the stigma they felt was attached to being from Camborne, the once thriving centre of the Cornish tin mining industry, which is now so run down. Their story is becoming well known, hence the TED talk, and they have been cited by the Council of Europe as an example of what towns should be doing for their young people to ensure they have access to opportunity and their social rights.

There is even a recommendation from the Council that all local authorities do something similar, and the day after my visit, two of the young people and David were off to Strasbourg to discuss progress and implementation. Connections being made from the town of Camborne to the centres of Europe and beyond.

David has been the mainstay of the school throughout the years and ensured its continuity. Several of the young people have played a big part and so have other adults, including Richard Carling who, as manager of one of the local supermarkets, became a big supporter and is currently the chair. And Hazel Stuteley has been at his elbow encouraging and advising him all the way.

David's chance encounter with Hazel was extraordinarily lucky because she has had a lifetime working in communities; first as a nurse, but more recently in helping communities to develop their own health programmes. Her philosophy is very simply that improved health – or health creation – comes from individuals and communities having a sense of mastery and control over their lives and environment. She and her organisation C2 Connecting Communities have had a quiet but powerful influence over many other health-creating developments around the country, including New NHS Alliance, which features in later chapters of this book.

I talked with the two University of Exeter researchers, Katrina Wyatt and Andrew Williams, who have been working with the TR14ers for some years. They told me that the group have transformed the lives of some of the young people involved and have led to measurable improvements in physical and mental health and confidence among the group as a whole, compared with children of similar age and background. Previous research found that there had also been a reduction in crime, complaints and antisocial behaviour.

Katrina's and Andrew's research aims to describe the value of having a group like the TR14ers and to identify the factors that have contributed to its adaptability and sustainability. They were particularly interested in how a community could generate its own health in a similar way, and in the values and leadership style practised by David and Hazel. This was, as they described it, facilitative, experimental and entrepreneurial. Things didn't proceed in a straight line from vision to plan to execution to results. But things were tried out, tested and sometimes rejected. It was learning by doing.

This gave the researchers a problem because it didn't fit with the standard academic and government methods of evaluating social programmes, which normally require pre-set targets and easily measurable outcomes. These methods inevitably lose much of the creativity, undervalue what is discovered through experimentation and, in this case, completely fail to present a full picture of what was happening with the TR14ers. And, perhaps most fundamentally, they simply can't get to grips with the important ideas of co-creating the future and of communities taking control and creating their own health.

This mismatch meant that the researchers had difficulty finding funding and, perhaps more importantly, were engaged with others around the country in struggling to break free and create a new and more useful evaluative approach. This is clearly needed.

There was similar contradiction in the way that the different authorities found it hard to understand the value of what David and the young people were doing. It didn't follow normal patterns and procedures and was based much more on creating relationships with the young people than on discipline and rules. It mirrored Mandy Wilton's approach in Cranbury College, where there was a relationship policy rather than a behavioural one.

And David was not the only one criticised by his managers for what he was doing. Richard Carling also had to handle complaints from his supermarket bosses for 'wasting' his time on this group when there were customers to pursue. There was apparently no point in him telling his superiors that helping to build the community was good for the company in the long run. He is now retired from the supermarket but still very much involved with the TR14ers as the chair of the board.

***

Schools, of course, have always had a major role in health and it is very good to see that in recent years there has been renewed emphasis on physical activity and diet. Many schools are rising to the challenge and following examples such as St Ninian's primary school in Stirling, Scotland where everyone, the head teacher and the smallest child included, run a mile each day during the lunch break. There are now hundreds of primary schools in the UK and abroad running the Daily Mile. And early evidence suggests there are benefits in fitness, body composition, sleep, diet, concentration, wellbeing and obesity.

Fitness and educational attainment improve together, as being healthy boosts your ability to learn. These are old ideas that are once more gaining traction. I recall that *mens sana in corpore sano* was written over the door of the gym at my own school years ago. A healthy mind in a healthy body. One of the ironies here, of course, is that educational authorities have been selling off school playing fields for years and the introduction of the national curriculum has led to a reduction in the amount of time children are physically active. This new emphasis on health is reversing the effects of these earlier policies.

I spoke to Julie Turner about this, a former head who was responsible for turning around a failing secondary school and is very familiar with the pressures in education. There were, she told me, many good things happening on health in mainstream education but they weren't widespread and really depended on the priorities of the head. Some carved out time for sport and exercise, as she had done, but others didn't or weren't able to do so.

There are, of course, academies, some with particular sport goals and some linked with local football and other sports clubs. And private schools have the financial means to do more, benefitting from better facilities and more time in a longer school day to devote to sport. But even when I visited a very successful academy, I was told about the increasing pressure on children and teachers. A pressure to perform. A pressure to be perfect.

Much of it came from outside school, from social media and friends and families. And, in too many cases, it is the result of problems at home, poverty, poor housing and other social factors. A great deal of stress also comes from the pressures to perform in school tests and, later in life, in the competition for jobs and careers. Julie told me that she worried about the quiet ones, the girls particularly. Resilience, she said, is key.

But for teachers, most of the pressure is generated within the system. Part of this is about funding and problems created by austerity, while a large part of the criticism I heard centred on the Office for Standards in Education, Children's Services and Skills (Ofsted). Schools have become helpless, in the face of national targets and inspections, Julie told me – but they are now fighting back. *'Ofsted can destroy people,'* she said. It is a very powerful statement coming from a head teacher who had succeeded in the system.

National policy underpins the whole education sector. And central to everything is the Ofsted inspection system. It has the laudable aim of improving standards but I heard it widely criticised within schools for stressing and demeaning teachers and, very importantly in this context, taking attention away from anything that is not included in its targets and measures, such as health.

Amanda Spielman, Ofsted's chief inspector, reveals a marked change in emphasis in her most recent report, published in January 2020. It shows that she and the organisation have heard the criticisms.

There are statements such as:

'... when measures and processes focus narrowly on outputs, such as exam results or testing, they can pull people's focus away from the substance.'

'… we found that school leaders were focused on increasing performance measures, too often to the detriment of much else. Teaching to the test, narrowing the curriculum, off-rolling and qualification gaming have become all too common.'

'We do acknowledge the role that strongly data driven accountability, including our own inspection frameworks, has played in distracting us collectively from the real substance of education.'

The report gives examples of some primary schools completely ignoring science lessons and focusing on the areas that will get them the best results in tests and inspections. This runs counter to common sense, let alone to the Government's commitment to promote STEM (Science, Technology, Engineering, Maths) subjects.

This is damning criticism from within the system itself. We will have to wait to see the Government's response to a problem which, if neglected, will continue to have long term impacts on health as well as on children's education, life chances and future prosperity.

Ideally, schools should have a major role in creating health. And, as part of this, it is important that pupils learn about physical and mental health and become, in the jargon, health literate. Phil Freeman, a very experienced teacher from Liverpool, told me: *'It's difficult for most of us to talk about our health and our feelings, and any worries we have about them, so you can use role play. Acting out visiting the doctor or a hospital and discussing how the different characters behave and react can help pupils think and learn. And they can be fun and memorable experiences too.'*

Schools can help improve health and education at the same time through activity, diet, activity in the open air, dance, music, and the other arts, as well as through the more formal content of taught lessons. And, as Phil reminded me, a lot of it can also be fun.

Pupils can also learn the vital soft skills they will need in later life. These are things like communication, leadership, teamwork, problem solving, flexibility, interpersonal skills, and even work ethic. These are every bit as important to employers as the content of lessons. Soft skills that aren't soft at all and certainly aren't easy. Phil and others have told me how depressing it is to see these skills undervalued and neglected, either not developed or treated as unimportant.

Social media have added to the stresses and anxieties of adolescence, as well as opening up new fields and knowledge to its users. Clinical depression and anxiety can be devastating and sometimes fatal if not treated. It is, however, very important to distinguish these conditions from the normal sadness and unhappiness we all experience at times in our lives and which can be magnified in adolescence. Even the most serious mental illnesses have better outcomes if they are recognised and tackled early while the brain is still developing.

The Charlie Waller Memorial Trust, which was set up in memory of a gifted young man who killed himself while depressed, provides evidence based training and resources for schools, colleges and universities, as well as digital resources including the Students Against Depression website. Young people can look after themselves by understanding better what's going on inside their minds and bodies.

The Trust has developed a national reputation, offering training and resources to GPs and practice nurses, as well as to schools, colleges and families, to understand and recognise mental illness early, building confidence and having practical tools to help. Too many young people have been falling through the net, the seriousness of their condition unrecognised or their families, friends and carers simply not knowing what to do to help.

It is interesting to note that the Trust is now going beyond training and support to helping schools develop the culture and programmes that will enable them to become truly health-creating environments. Being active and not just reactive.

***

There's another issue here too.

We expect all children to go down the same academic route, regardless of their skills and aptitudes. It is right to encourage academic excellence, but it won't suit everyone.

Employers are often as interested in EQ, emotional intelligence, as in IQ. And there is a move among entrepreneurial organisations to recognise and value AQ, adversity intelligence, perhaps better described as resilience. Some psychologists now also recognise physical, creativity and spiritual intelligence as well (PQ, CQ and SQ) and see IQ as contributing only 20 per cent to success in later life. Whatever one's view of this plethora of indices, the last point about IQ being only a partial indicator of ability and success seems like plain common sense.

I was reminded of my time with the TR14ers in Camborne when I visited the North West Training Council in Liverpool, where they train apprentices in a wide range of disciplines. There was the same emphasis on listening to people, on providing opportunity, and on playing to their strengths.

I knew that the teachers I had been talking to in mainstream schools had exactly the same emphasis, but I had begun to realise that they were handicapped by not being able to offer the full range of opportunities to their students. The concentration on academic subjects and the pressure of testing and exams means that a wide range of talents, strengths and passions are ignored or downplayed.

It is a very narrow gate that we expect all our children to go through. A system that, on the face of it, is all about encouraging success and achievement but, in reality, turns out to be about stress and failure for too many.

Despite the efforts of people such as the former Education Secretary Lord Kenneth Baker, vocational education is another area where successive governments have failed. There has been some movement with improvements in apprenticeships and a new requirement that all schools must offer pupils information about technical education. But more needs to be done to improve the opportunities for vocational education.

***

'My life began on 16 July 1978.'
I could guess what was coming next.
'That was when I left school and started my apprenticeship.'
The speaker was one of the instructors at the North West Training Council in Liverpool. We were talking in a room that had a large number

of electrical circuits attached to upright boards on the walls. Each board was about three foot square, with seven or eight items fixed to it. They were linked together by wires, junction boxes, switches, fuses and other components, and mimicked the wiring you might find in a house or an office. I could see that the board immediately behind the instructor had a notice attached to it saying *'Danger, faulty circuit.'*

This was the assessment room where the apprentices had to demonstrate their skills in fault tracing and repair. It was where the apprentice electricians learned the skills they needed to sort out the tangle of wiring in the attic, work out why light bulbs kept blowing, and deal with the intermittent fault in the office heating system.

I met some of the apprentices in the room next door, where they were each working on their own board, wiring up the components and checking they were safely installed. They showed me what they were doing, talking me through their actions. One young woman showed me how she was preparing a detailed drawing of the circuit she was going to install. Applied logic really, carefully worked through on the basis of a set of learned principles.

I started out by asking each of them why they had wanted to do an apprenticeship, but I stopped after a while. The details were different but the sense was the same in every case. This was what they wanted to be doing. They were creating their own future.

The centre's chief executive, Paul Musa, gave me a tour of the building and recalled his own story. He had completed an apprenticeship with the predecessor organisation 30 years ago and came back later as an instructor. Nobody knew the organisation better than him. He was passionate about the centre and what it was doing.

Apprenticeships aren't a new idea and local employers had founded the centre almost 60 years earlier to cater for their needs. Local industry and its requirements had changed. Now, many of the apprentices were in the food and hospitality industry rather than heavy engineering, and the centre was installing robotics as it kept pace with the changing workplace. 5G and the Internet of Things will bring further radical changes during the working lives of these apprentices.

The centre had to make its way in the world without a guaranteed supply of apprentices from a group of employers. It was always seen, however, as an important local resource and had received support from the combined boroughs – the five local boroughs that make up Merseyside. It's now an independent charity. A leading local councillor, Sir Ron Wilson, a trustee of the centre and a powerful local advocate, accompanied us on our visit.

Paul and Ron told me about the financial issues they faced and the complexities of working with government where – as frequently happens – change may suddenly be made to systems and processes that affect, among other things, their income and viability. They were, however, more complimentary about Ofsted than others had been, seeing it as a critical friend.

Paul told me that the centre has good support systems in place for people who need help with their health or other issues. But what really struck me was the atmosphere of the whole centre – purposeful, achieving, nurturing, people working to their strengths. And creating health. Such a contrast to what I was being told was true of some schools and other institutions.

It seems to me, as an outsider, that one of the paradoxes of the whole education system is that it has become so focused on reacting to problems rather than anticipating and dealing with them before they manifest. The education system writ large has many professionals with expertise in dealing with all aspects of child and adolescent development. There are, of course, variations from area to area and austerity has reduced their availability. However, should not more be done to make schools the health creators they could be?

It reminds me of how health systems operate. Aaron Motsoaledi, when he was health minister in South Africa, said to me: *'Why do we pay the people who prevent diabetes a small amount, the people who treat diabetes a larger amount, and the people who treat the complications of diabetes a very large amount. What if it was the other way around?'*

What if the incentives in our systems really were the other way around?

***

Looking back at this and the last chapter, it seems that government has lost its way on education policy. There are obvious problems in its policies on exclusion, inspection and vocational education. With a record like this the state should exercise its power with great humility. It needs to make space for everyone as equal partners.

This chapter recommends that the Government urgently change its policies in two important areas. Firstly, it should *review and change the Ofsted inspection system to ensure that its assessments focus on the real substance of education and not on achievement against narrow test results*. Secondly, it should *improve and increase the amount of vocational education opportunities available to children within the school system*.

It is too easy to write young people off, particularly if they don't fit in with our norms and systems. The keys to success in Camborne, Liverpool and Reading appear to be to listen to young people, encourage their aspirations, and build on their strengths.

This is another of our very simple big ideas: *build on people's strengths*. These strengths are very easy to overlook when it is the negatives and the problems that are always presented to us, perhaps because they seem more newsworthy.

A clearer picture is emerging from these last three chapters of what we need to do to take back control of our health. Take off our NHS spectacles and with them our preconceptions and prejudices. Concentrate on developing relationships and less on systems and rules. Build on strengths not weaknesses.

These actions all go against the grain of current practice, but they all offer hope.

CHAPTER SIX
FREE RANGE CHILDREN

Hayley Mitchell had very deliberately taken control of her son's health when she and Lizzy Hassay set up Free Range Urban Kids (FRUK) in Hackney five years ago.

I visited them on a damp, chilly morning in January. The sort of day when many children wouldn't have wanted to venture out into the playground, but here were 14 children aged from three to six playing happily outdoors. *'There's no such thing as bad weather,'* I had been told before I went there, *'only the wrong clothing.'* And here they were, well wrapped up, faces glowing and mostly already good and muddy.

They were playing inside a fenced-off enclosure of perhaps half an acre in a large public park, rather hidden away behind the tennis and basketball courts. There was a fringe of tall trees at one end providing a windbreak and other clumps of trees and bushes on two of the sides. Hayley took me to meet a group of six children who were playing on a large log, which was lying on its side and about as tall as them. They were climbing onto it, jumping off, or propelling themselves down two old wooden forms that they were using as improvised slides.

They came and went, playing alone or together, sometimes just sitting on top of the log and surveying the world, lost in thought, or digging their fingers into the wood where it was starting to rot, flaking pieces off. This was all child-led play, Janine, one of the staff members, explained. She told me some of their names, Will and Katia and Mo, before the children joined in giving each other different names. *'No, this is Katia,'* and *'He's John'* and *'She's Lally.'* Teasing Janine and me. It was that sort of day. A day for doing nothing really, just messing around.

There was a water area under one group of trees where they could make mud pies if they wanted and splash around. There were no toys as such, just things they found to play with, along with a few containers and a box. It was a place for picking up leaves, jumping in puddles, making dens, encountering beetles and worms, chasing around in the wind, the sun and the rain. A childhood in touch with nature – and one you felt instinctively was good for the spirits and the soul, as well as the immune system, the lungs and the heart.

There was also a box with a few tools they could use with one to one supervision. Hayley told me there were risks but they were managed. Sometimes they would have a fire, too. Learning to light it safely and put it out afterwards. On other days they might go out for a walk together, along to Hackney Marshes and the nature reserve.

On the other side of the enclosure, half hidden by trees, were three small tents, upright sentry boxes containing potties and somewhere to change the children's clothes if needed. A tarpaulin was stretched across a seating area where everyone could retreat if the weather got really wild and eat the packed lunches their parents had prepared.

Hayley and Lizzy set up FRUK when their children were very young. Hayley's motivation, she told me, was about giving her youngest child the start in life she wanted for him. As she said, it was really about her taking control. Something she felt that she hadn't been able to do with her older child.

Hayley had previously worked in marketing and public relations for global fashion brands, and Lizzy was an accountant and business adviser. So, while they knew something about running a business, this was a total change of direction for them both. But it was all going very well and there had been a good demand for places from the start. They were now expanding their activities to include an after school club and a holiday class. The Covid-19 crisis has, of course, put all their plans on hold for the time being.

FRUK is for children aged between three and seven but they had also started a nature class for older kids, aged between eight and 11. They had also recently run an evening session in the dark, which had gone down very well with the children. Exciting and a little bit scary, torches flashing in the darkness, everything looking strange, and different animals, insects and noises to look and listen out for.

I asked Hayley what impact FRUK was having on the children and their health. They were fitter and stronger because of all the physical activity, she said. And more resilient. It built up their strength. She told me, too, that the children were more confident as a result of learning to do things and not being cosseted all the time. It was quite something, she said, watching a four year old using a tool confidently or whittling a shape out of twig with a knife while observing all the safety rules.

And in five years they hadn't once had an outbreak of illness spreading among the group – some bug being passed from one to another – as can happen all too easily in a confined indoor environment.

I was told by another mother, whose child had been part of the group for three years, that her son had developed a real sense of direction. He knew where things were in the neighbourhood and felt part of it all. He could show her the path to get to the marshes or other local places. It was so different, she said, from her own childhood, homebound, telly always on, ferried around by car, and no real sense of the place where she lived.

And, Hayley told me, their approach helped children build up their core strength. Some children she knew arrived at school very weak from how they had been brought up, unable to sit upright at a desk, take part in games or hold a pen. They had spent all their time slouched in front of a screen at home. They were at an immediate disadvantage, not ready to get the most from their new environment. And some of them weren't ready in other ways. They would have false starts and fail to settle, sometimes being taken out of school altogether and returning a few months later. Children need to be ready for school before they get there.

Children can also become less fit again when they are in full time school. Hayley notices this in her eight year old son, whom, she said, is now at primary school and is more likely to get agitated. Sadly, it's part of a national trend with studies showing that children do less exercise as they get older. An hour a week less when they are 11 than when they were six.

FRUK is a forest school and part of a national and global movement that started in the 1990s. There are now agreed definitions and principles for what makes a forest school and standardised training. Different forest schools cater for different ages of children and not everything has to be done outside all the time. Most of the children at FRUK attend two or three days a week. As the Forest School Association says: *'Forest school … offers all learners regular opportunities to achieve and develop confidence and self-esteem through hands-on learning experiences in a woodland or natural environment with trees.'*

Forest schools are part of a long and distinguished tradition: the Scouts and Guides movements, the Woodcraft Folk, and many others. They tap into some of the same motivations and practices as outdoor education and school visits to farms and the countryside. This is all good for the health of the children but it also helps instil a love for nature and the environment.

But there's also something all too real that has disappeared. Generation by generation our children have been increasingly confined to the space around their own homes. A study of four generations in Sheffield is typical of the change: at the age of ten the great grandfather could travel up to six miles from home by himself, his child could go about one and a half miles, the grandchild three or four streets, and today's ten year old little farther than the garden.

There aren't many free range kids anymore.

Apart, of course, from some of the ones excluded from school whom I mentioned in Chapter 4, and whom the head teacher described as just disappearing.

***

My visit to FRUK reminded me of what Amanda Gummer of Fundamentally Children had told me about the need for a balanced play diet. Amanda is a child psychologist who designed the diet as a practical aid for parents to work out the best way for their children to spend their time – and, in particular, how to limit the amount of screen time their children enjoyed.

She used the concept of a diet because we are all familiar with the idea that we need some fat, sugars and salt, as well everything else, as part of a healthy balanced diet. Screen time is, in effect, the sugar or salt in the play diet. We need some but the temptation is to have too much. Similarly, children need part of their time to be organised – music lessons perhaps, gym classes, ballet and rugby – but they also need to be allowed to do nothing, run around, play and just be children.

Amanda splits the diet up into four groups. The first part is active free play and imaginative play. The child doing what they want. This, of course, is where a forest school would fit in. Amanda describes this as the superfood of the play diet and suggests that it should be a big part of the daily routine. The next part is team games, board games, construction, reading and creative play. This is more organised and often goal-oriented. The third part is educational toys and games, including digital ones. It's mostly quiet and solitary play but with clear learning outcomes. The final part is passive screen time, TV and solitary video games. Children should regularly get a bit from each group. It's all about getting the balance right between the different types of play.

Amanda is careful to point out that what children want to do and how they develop are personal and about individual personalities, capabilities and choices. Developmental milestones are only guidelines. All children are different and develop at their own pace. And looking back at the forest schools, not every child will thrive in them, enjoy playing in the rain and puddles, or relish their first encounters with beetles and worms.

The balanced play diet is designed to make sense of the endless amount of advice with which parents are bombarded – whether from official, charitable or commercial sources. We live in a world that is increasingly competitive, for ourselves and our children. Are we getting it right?

Am I failing as a parent? It is all too easy to feel out of control and to lose confidence in yourself.

Forest schools emphasise the importance of being child led but Amanda also points to the importance of parent-led childcare. Parents have to make many health choices: about diet, when to call for help and, of course, about vaccination and treatments. Families and friends are vital. There are support groups for parents in many communities: some formal organisations like Sure Start, other community networks, and informal mothers' groups too. All of these can help parents become more 'health literate' and take control of their and their children's health. But it's still not easy.

I twice heard on my travels a story about a young woman pushing a pram or a pushchair while wearing headphones and, in effect, ignoring her child. It's a seductive image, a negative meme, tapping into our prejudices and feeding our fears about technology and alienation.

But another young mother said to me: *'Maybe, but what was she doing just before she put the headphones on?'*

She sent me a WhatsApp message with an image of a drawing showing everything the mother was probably doing before she set off to the shops with the pushchair. The feeding, the playing, the changing the nappy, the clearing up, the feeding again, the washing, the playing with the child and her sister, who had now been dropped off at the nursery, the clearing up again … but need I go on?

How easy it is to set up such a meme and be judgemental. *'Maybe,'* the young mother said to me, *'she is slowly dying inside.'* The pressure to be perfect isn't just for children. It extends fully to parents.

Parents also need access to health services. Most parents go back to work after maternity or paternity leave, leaving their young child at nursery, playgroup or with a childminder, and it is vital that they can get help from the NHS when they need it. The NHS and local surgeries need to make health services more accessible to working parents and enable them to use them via phone and the internet, and at evenings and weekends.

Erika Brodnock's own experience of postnatal depression prompted her to do something about it. Roughly five out of six women, she told me, experience depression at some point when they go back to work after the birth of a child. It is an enormous and still largely hidden problem. And, of course, nothing to do with how tough you are or how strongminded.

Like others in this book, Erika turned for help to the professionals and she also recognised the potential of new technologies to enhance existing medical care. But what, she wondered, if we could learn in real time about what works. Much of the advice and support was based on old research and every generation of mothers experience different circumstances. Life moves on at a great pace. Her solution was to look at what is happening now, and to use artificial intelligence to capture what professionals are doing and how they are working with their clients today.

Erika co-founded Kami to take these ideas forward. It now has a network of 40 mothers helping her and professionals to design the whole approach. They are using AI to scan recordings of consultations, picking out the themes and linking them with what both the mothers and the professionals experience. The aim is to produce much better tailored counselling and support for mothers and their partners, and which are firmly based in today's reality. By using the power of artificial intelligence in this way, Erika also expects to be able to provide support for parents in currently underserved areas and communities across the UK.

Erika wants to make the learning available to academics and the NHS, but she also wants to market it to employers so that they can tackle postnatal depression in the workplace, with all the benefits that will bring to them and their employees. It is the same sort of balance between public and private benefit that many social entrepreneurs adopt. It is not the traditional idea of private companies supporting charities with part of their profits but a much more intimate connection between private and public good, and something we will return to in Chapter 10.

Forest schools are private, so parents have to pay for them. They are out of the reach of many. Almost one in five children in the UK are living in poverty, many of them badly fed and living in poor housing. There are many things that the Government can and should do to alleviate this, but one central and empowering action would be to provide more childcare support for working parents.

Lack of childcare is both a constant source of stress for working parents – always worried that it might disappear at short notice – and limits the amount of time parents can work and therefore earn. It is perhaps the single biggest thing the Government could do to enable parents to gain greater control of their own lives and enable them to provide the support their children need to become healthy future citizens.

And parent-led childcare seems like a good idea.

***

It's even harder, of course, for parents whose children are different in any way. Helen Needham only realised that she herself was autistic two years ago when her son was diagnosed with the condition. She has a successful career as a consultant in financial services and the diagnosis explained a lot to her about herself. She has since learned new skills in how to manage her life.

We had arranged to meet to discuss her experience as a parent of a child with autism. Shortly before our meeting she sent me an email: *'I wanted to let you know that I sometimes struggle with social anxiety and making small talk with people I don't know, especially in unfamiliar situations. I don't think it should be a problem today as we have met briefly before but want to let you know in case I struggle to get my words out when we first meet.'*

In the event we talked easily, and it was evident that Helen had found her own ways to cope. She wanted to see me because she was passionate about changing the way society treats people who are *'neurodivergent'* and hoped I could help through Parliament. Her son had had a lot of bad experiences in his short life and had been, in her words, *'pushed out'* of school at the age of six.

Professionals, she told me, judge the behaviour not the circumstances. And parents become angry and wound up about it because they are not listened to, so the whole situation can get out of hand. There's an early assessment process, which is designed to signpost the family towards continuing help. However, she told me, a lack of resources means there are long wait times and families often have to fight for an assessment.

Moreover, each professional does their assessment independently, which reduces the value of multidisciplinary assessments.

But the fundamental difficulty, she said, is that *'they try to fix the behaviour but not the environment'*. The focus needs to be on people and environment interactions and not just on the person.

Helen runs a website, Me.Decoded, which is designed to publish *'personal stories from the neurodivergent and allies, in the pursuit of decoding neurodiversity'*. She is using it to build awareness of autism, attention deficit disorder, OCD, dyslexia and other conditions, so that the general public and professionals can understand them better and relate to people who have them more easily. She is also campaigning for change.

She wants to see better workplace inclusion for people who are neurodivergent, as well as changes in schools. She wants less of just putting people in silos and trying to modify their behaviour, and more emphasis on their interaction with the environment. She wants the public and professionals to understand better these invisible differences. And, most of all, she wants children like her son not to be limited by their condition – and to be able to realise their potential.

***

These early years are the foundation for health. Our future health is quite literally made in the womb and in the first few years of life. Our mother's mental and physical health affect us, and so does our diet and our social and physical environment. Overeating and obesity when very young increase the likelihood of a heart attack as an adult. Absent or inconsistent parenting, neglect or abuse can mean children don't form an attachment with anyone early in their lives. In turn, this makes it very difficult or impossible to form relationships later and can lead to all kinds of other difficulties.

There has been a big movement across the country to try to head off these problems. Sure Start in England and related programmes in the rest of the UK were developed from the late 1990s, with the aim of giving children the best possible start in life through improvement of childcare, early education, health and family support, along with an emphasis on outreach and community development. Various reviews have shown their impact on, among other things, reducing expenditure on the NHS.

However, central government funding was cut in the austerity drive of the last decade and many programmes and centres were closed. Sure Start is arguably one of the most important casualties of austerity.

The Early Intervention Foundation was set up in 2013 to focus on intervening in the lives of young children seen as being vulnerable and at risk. It describes its work as about reducing the risk factors and increasing the protective factors in a child's life, and it has supported projects throughout the country. Cities, counties and boroughs as diverse as Nottingham, Norfolk, and Barking and Dagenham have started their own early intervention programmes.

More than ten years ago, the Scottish Government created its Early Years Initiative with the aim of making Scotland the best place in the world to grow up. Wonderfully ambitious, it brought together national government departments with local government and other agencies into a shared plan, which recognised that they each had their role to play. They worked together to identify the major opportunities and problem areas and reviewed the evidence of what worked.

Their interventions were carefully mapped out and targeted, with each agency taking action. One of the most effective things, however, was simply to encourage parents to read their children a bedtime story every night. Those regular few minutes of warm intimacy are therapeutic in every sense.

As we have seen before, such simple and commonsense actions, which seem so small to a professional, can make a real difference in people's lives. Children need adult attention. They need cuddling, talking to and listening to. They need love as much in Glasgow as in the slums of Colombia described in Chapter 4. They need to do things with others. They need people. And they need consistency, routine and, as far as possible, an ordered life. There is science and evidence behind it, too.

Sir Harry Burns, who was chief medical officer in Scotland at the time and played a leading role in developing the Early Years Initiative, explains that '... *a chaotic early life leads to a reduced ability to manage stress and behave appropriately ... the biology is very clear: chaotic difficult circumstances lead to increased risk of physical ill health'.*

He continues: *'So let's not spend a fortune trying to find drugs to fix that. Let's change the chaotic and difficult circumstances so that they don't happen.'*

And the financial consequences are dramatic. Harry told me that adverse childhood events – the technical name for the whole range of traumatic and stressful events, from the death of a parent to abuse and neglect that adversely affect a child's health and life chances – will cost Scotland about £3.5 billion over their lifetime for each year group. It is a dramatic reminder of John Bird's 'millionaire' *Big Issue* sellers.

Harry is understandably proud of what the Early Years Initiative achieved in improving the health of the youngest children. However, he questions whether it was wise to expand it in recent years, from a focused programme dealing with the youngest children into a very broad based set of programmes for children up to the age of 18 and with many more sets of targets. He fears it has been reduced into being all about targets and management when, as he puts it, it is really about relationships.

He believes that these targets miss out the key element of the community and the importance of the relationships between individuals within a community. He stresses that the key point is people need to be in control of their lives and in a stable community.

He directed me to a TED talk he had given, in which he quoted Jimmy Reid as Lord Rector of Glasgow University talking about alienation, which he defined as the cry of men who are the victims of blind economic forces beyond their control. It is the sense of despair and hopelessness that pervades people, who feel with justification that they have no say in shaping or determining their own destinies.

Harry went on to say: *'This is what I think is happening in West Central Scotland. The cycle of alienation that may begin with chaotic early years leads to mental health and ... behaviour problems at school. And, by the way, when a child who is becoming alienated has behaviour problems at school, what do we do with them? We exclude them from school, alienating them even further.'*

There are echoes here of the earlier discussion about children excluded from school. There are also echoes of Helen Needham's campaign on autism and her insistence that it is the interactions between the person and the environment that matter. You can't just try to tackle the behaviour. It is about people and their community.

*****

The saying *Health is made at home, hospitals are for repairs* comes from an idealised version of an African village where children grow up as part of a multi-generational loving family, have siblings and friends they can play with outdoors, and are part of a wider community with its own structures and social norms, where all adults have some responsibility for all children. It is an environment where they can grow up healthily, as well as learn social skills and other vital lessons in living.

Few if any African villages are really like this, of course, and it is not how British children grow up either. Here, most of us live in a small nuclear family, some with only one parent or a shifting cast of adults. Few of us live in such strong communities and most children spend much of their time before they go to school in their own home, depending on how much time their busy parents can find to do things with them.

Nevertheless, there are many aspects of this idealised picture that are still very important to us: playing, being outdoors, closeness to our family, friends and other adults. And the strong and stable community to which Sir Harry Burns refers. All of these things are about *making* health – healthy people in a health-creating society. And all of them take pressure off the NHS.

There is only space in this chapter to highlight a small part of the remarkable work that so many individuals and organisations are doing to develop healthy young children, or to repair and limit the damage that, in Harry's words, the *'chaotic and difficult circumstances'* in which they live may be doing to them. These are stories of hope and optimism but they are also reminders of pain and difficulty, and of the inequalities that blight our country.

This is all about health creation and creating the conditions in which people can live healthy lives. There are private entrepreneurs here, voluntary organisations, campaigning groups, and local and national governments. Some involve health professionals, and some, such as Helen Needham's Me.Decoded, wish they could get them involved. All of them are about people taking control, acting for themselves and not just reacting.

These stories pick up themes from other chapters, such as the importance of relationships, mental health, and playing to people's strengths rather than reinforcing their weaknesses. They also introduce another of the big ideas in health creation: *the role of the community.* It is a theme we will return to frequently in the following chapters, as we make the links between healthy individuals and healthy communities, and between healthy communities and a healthy planet.

CHAPTER SEVEN

MEANING AND PURPOSE IN LATER LIFE

The last three chapters were about children and teenagers and helping them to develop into confident and capable adults. This one is about not losing control and confidence as we become older, not becoming the passive recipients of care and attention.

Or, as the title of Sir Muir Gray's book on healthy ageing has it, *Sod 70!* He argues we should abolish the word *'care'*, as it gives us the wrong idea about old age.

We must turn the idea that old people are in need of help all the time on its head and recognise that they are often leaders and innovators who enjoy healthy and fulfilled lives. We may well get slower, have less energy, and suffer more ailments as we live longer. However, Muir points out that most of what happens is not the normal biological process of ageing but is due to loss of fitness and disease and most of this, in turn, is caused by the environment we live in, our behaviour and negative thinking.

For many people, the most pressing obligations of children and work are out of the way by the age of 70, and we can be freer to choose what we do, maybe even reinvent ourselves. Many others, of course, may still find these freedoms constrained by caring for parents and older relatives. And lockdowns, of course, limit what is possible. They also damage health by reducing physical activity and increasing isolation, thereby accelerating cognitive decline.

Some older people need help, of course, and we will probably all need support at some point. There are big differences, too, between the experiences of the better off, with their comfortable retirements and holiday plans, and people living on the state pension or benefits with chronic illnesses and little to look forward to. And lockdown has only widened the gap.

I was reminded of the possibilities of older age when I talked to Paula Gamester about the Sewing Rooms and the Silver Sewers. Paula has been a keen seamstress all her life and creative too, challenging boundaries. She told me how her first venture into design was when she altered her school uniform at Liverpool's Notre Dame Catholic College. She had gone to school one day in navy blue hot pants. The nuns promptly sent her home.

After some years working abroad in a variety of jobs, Paula was back in Merseyside and working at a chamber of commerce when she became inspired by the idea of social businesses. She set up the Sewing Rooms in 2010 as a community interest company, combining her love of sewing with her business skills. The company, based in Skelmersdale, employs local people to fulfil contracts from companies around the country, including suppliers for John Lewis and other major stores. She has more recently set up a bespoke curtain making service. And the Sewing Rooms now provides training courses for people of all ages and backgrounds.

It's all about *'trade to tackle social problems'*, she said. She uses the profits from the business to support various local groups and bring people together, and she has also supplied school uniforms to people who needed them. It's about bringing money into the town, she told me, creating jobs and boosting the local economy. But for her, the biggest issue is confidence. Self-confidence and the belief in yourself – an underlying theme throughout this book.

Paula set up the Silver Sewers group five years ago to bring together lonely and isolated older women. It has been an enormous success with regular meetings, but it has also had an unexpected result. The Silver

Sewers really came into their own when Paula decided to run a sewing project for Syrian women refugees arriving in the town. Basing it on principles of mindfulness, Paula and her colleagues created a calming environment for the women with music playing in the background.

Paula also invited the Silver Sewers to these sessions, hoping they would mix and maybe form friendships. It worked far better than she imagined. The Sewers really took the refugees under their wing. They started to bring cakes in every week and the refugees responded with sweets they had made. Over time, the Sewers provided clothing, friendship and helped the refugees learn English.

Here was something else the Sewers could do, and maybe only they could do. They had the time to be friends and, importantly, they did not feel threatened by the new arrivals or seem threatening to the refugees.

The Silver Sewers model is replicable, and Paula has generously provided support for another group in Halton, on the other side of Merseyside, which has set up their own Sewing Rooms social business. And the idea of older people supporting refugees is replicable too.

***

As Muir Gray points out in *Sod 70!* it is never too late to take preventive action, to get fit and eat well. In fact, walking and activity will improve health and life expectancy at every age. Starting in your eighties is better than not starting at all.

Muir explains that ageing is not a disease to be treated but a set of natural processes. Scientists are beginning to understand them, with the prospect that regenerative medicine may lead to people living far longer and far healthier. Perhaps the first person to live to 150 has already been born.

However, Muir points out that the more important issue is to live healthier longer, compressing the period of dependency and disability at the end of life, and increase 'healthspan' rather than lifespan. And, he argues, this means tackling three other processes that we can control now: loss of fitness, preventable disease and negative beliefs.

Being active – physically, emotionally and cognitively – is crucial. Muir, just like the ancient Greeks, is a great advocate of walking, especially brisk walking, and calls diabetes the walking disease. As Hippocrates said more than 2000 years ago: *'Walking is the best medicine.'* It is a message for all ages – and all ages.

Activity is not, however, the whole story. A social circle is also important for our wellbeing. Loneliness is an emotional issue and can be a source of great unhappiness for people of any age, with some groups of younger people more affected than older ones. There is evidence that, in terms of health, loneliness can make people more susceptible to illness and slow recovery. The Government and others have developed strategies and plans to reduce loneliness and it has become quite a high-profile concern. However, we need to be careful not to turn it into a medical condition and try to treat it as such, but recognise instead that it is a consequence of a changing society – with, for example, more marital breakups, and changes in family roles and employment practices – and can only be addressed through further changes in society.

As Muir points out, it is when loneliness becomes real social isolation that it is an active danger to health. Isolation leads to changes in the brain. These are now known to be precursors to the changes brought about by dementia, which in turn brings with it awful personal and financial costs.

Even more important appears to be having a purpose or meaning in life. A reason to get up in the morning. Learning something, campaigning, working with others on things you are interested in or care about. All of them, incidentally, counteracting some of the ill effects of loneliness. The purpose could be anything from caring for the cat, to wanting to see the grandchildren, to painting or translating poetry from ancient Greek – or perhaps into it. The idea that meaning and purpose are important is now well accepted medically. Indeed, a recent article in the *Journal of the American Medical Association* concluded that there is a significant association between life purpose and mortality. Its title *Renewing purpose, building and sustaining social engagement, and embracing a positive lifestyle* really says it all.

The University of the Third Age is perhaps the longest established national body run by and for older people that offers both a social circle and a meaning or purpose. It was founded 35 years ago as *a 'UK movement of retired and semi-retired people, who come together to continue their educational, social and creative interests in a friendly and informal environment'*. It is an informal organisation made up of local groups, of which there are now more than 1000 with about 450,000 members between them. The local groups determine what they do and how. The members organise the courses and programmes, and often provide the lecturers as well as the participants.

The University is constantly forward looking and defines itself *'by the experiences still to explore'* and not by the age of its members or the experiences of the past. Its own research demonstrates the impact of its activities on confidence, self-esteem and wellbeing.

Many of the University's activities involve creativity or the arts in some way. The arts bring joy and enrichment to our lives and, as a consequence, have health and wellbeing benefits. As we age, involvement with the arts helps to overcome loneliness and social isolation and offers meaning, as well as the intrinsic value of the activity. Art for its own sake.

Participants in arts activities report a sense of purpose, professionalism and responsibility that have largely been absent since they retired from work. There are older people's dance and theatre groups, which provide physical activity as well as the satisfaction from participation. And something like attending a life drawing class involves a combination of learning, psychomotor skills, and being physically and socially active. It is perhaps no surprise that arts and creativity figure in so many of the stories in this book.

There are other programmes and schemes where older people can volunteer as 'grandparents' to young children and families, providing some stability and support, and sharing their experience of life. Others may wish to teach young people, volunteer in the NHS, or run events in their neighbourhood or village.

Volunteering in any of these ways provides a purpose and a social circle and, as evidence shows, is two way with benefits to both parties. I am not the only one who has visited a day centre for older people and been struck by how the helpers were often older than the clients.

Or to have seen people in their eighties and nineties doggedly continuing as secretaries, treasurers or members of charities. They have a reason to get up in the morning.

These ideas are brought together very neatly in The Challenge Hub. Its founder Richard Pertwee defines its purpose in very simple terms: *'encouraging people over the age of 55 to lead the fullest life and so to help others'.*

Richard was motivated by research showing the difficulties faced by many in achieving a healthy and productive retirement. He realised that people in later years do not have any widely recognised reference point to which they can turn for inspiration, or any sense of what is 'normal' or 'expected' as they move towards retirement. There is no signposting for older people such as there is for younger people through school, Scouts, National Citizenship Service, Duke of Edinburgh's Award, Cadet Corps, or other organisations on offer.

Richard had originally conceived of the Hub as a sort of Duke of Edinburgh's Award for older people: something that challenged you and did some good for society at the same time. Run off a Mumsnet-type platform, which allows members to exchange experiences and ideas, the Hub challenges people to achieve targets they set for themselves in the three areas of learning, physical activity and doing something for others.

The challenge, called *The All in One*, grades individual challenges by difficulty and uses a points system. Learning could, for example, be anything from bricklaying to speaking Portuguese. The physical challenge might extend from a series of park runs to a 200 mile walk. Social contribution is about giving at least two hours each week to any charity or community interest company for varying numbers of weeks. It's your choice and you can set the challenge level to suit your ability and take account of any disability you may have. The essential point is that the task you take on must be a real challenge for you – and a true achievement when you have completed it.

Richard is a retired corporate lawyer from the City of London who has spent the last few years working with a variety of voluntary organisations. He sees the Hub as being of particular benefit to people who are just retiring and are looking for something to do as they work out how they are going to live the next stage of their lives. It is a time of uncertainty as well as opportunity for many people: a point in their lives when they can redirect their energies and perhaps even reinvent themselves. And, as Richard points out, people who embark from the outset on a positive and socially engaged retirement are most likely to remain mentally and physically healthy for longest.

There can be, in his words, *'a loss of purpose and status but also the loss to society of all that accumulated wisdom and knowledge'*.

These are powerful points. The Hub encourages people to try things out and see what they really enjoy. And people who sign up don't have to commit to finishing a challenge or even to starting one. It will be a success if the experience helps them in any way work through their future. And, of course, it should be fun, as well as good for their physical and mental health.

The Challenge Hub is very versatile. Richard is already working with a large Welsh NHS trust on its pre-retirement programmes, and with one of the UK's leading providers of retirement housing, which wants to build a sense of community within a retirement village with a shared challenge. The Hub can also offer a social prescribing service. Perhaps in future, primary care nurses and doctors can prescribe a challenge rather than medicines.

The Hub is not limited to people retiring but provides an opportunity for anyone 55 and over to link with others, share and join in some structured activities. It's early days with the Hub just getting off the ground but it looks as if it has all the right ingredients, and Richard is reaching out to organisations to work with him and involve more people from all different backgrounds around the country.

He told me that the Duke of Edinburgh Awards enrol more than 250,000 young people every year. It's a target for him too: a challenge.

One of the themes underlying all the programmes, projects and activities described here is to be imaginative and to think the unthinkable. Take ideas to the extreme.

And with technology, of course, the extremes can quickly become the new normal. There have long been call buttons and other assistive technology in people's houses, enabling them to get help when they need it. Newer developments, such as robots and wearable technology, will allow people to do much more for themselves as they age – staying in control – and monitoring and responding to changes in their health. And the design of buildings, communities and equipment can all contribute to older people living life to the full.

AI and machine learning have an enormous amount to offer. Richard Howells is a tech entrepreneur whose mother became ill. She lives in rural Shropshire, a place that Richard discovered was a 'care blackspot' with very little support available to her. How he not only solved his mother's problem but is also beginning to change the way care is delivered across the whole country is described in Chapter 11.

Sir Muir Gray, too, has plans to use technology to help people stay active and engaged. Why not, he asks, create a virtual book group, where members wearing virtual reality headsets meet up from their own homes – perhaps while self-isolating? What about such a group visiting Venice together, wearing their headsets and walking at their own pace around the house or on a treadmill while simultaneously walking together through St Mark's Square? These and many other ideas are within reach.

The ability to navigate the web and explore cyber space and virtual reality have become ever more important – even without a viral pandemic to stimulate interest. There is a danger, however, of a double digital divide between the more and the less affluent and well educated, a gap reinforced for older people who, typically, have less access to and familiarity with such technology. Age UK has responded by setting up a 'digital buddy' scheme, which sees younger people help older ones gain access to and learn about this new dimension in our lives. But a large part of the problem will remain as discussed below.

***

The evidence of what enables people to be active and healthy into old age is already available. Some of it is anecdotal but, increasingly, there are systematic studies that show the benefit of different activities.

Lord Geoffrey Filkin of the All-Party Parliamentary Group on Longevity took me through it. Geoff was a minister in the last Labour Government and has a background in housing and local government. He has played a leading role in developing new thinking on ageing in recent years.

The All-Party Group's focus is on public policy and how it needs to change to meet the Government's ambitious aim of ensuring that people have five extra years of healthy independent lives by 2035. And like others, the Group wants to change the language and the narrative, making us think differently about older age. They want to change *'the problem of ageing into the opportunity of longevity'*.

There is a broad consensus about the main parameters of healthy ageing, as Geoff explained. Being reasonably healthy and having an adequate income are key, and then comes the trio of purpose, social relationships and physical activity. He also stressed the importance of starting early, before you are 65, and preparing for older age, as Richard Pertwee has suggested. Sitting alongside all these vital points, however, is the social gradient identified by Sir Michael Marmot: the enormous inequality in health between people of different wealth and status.

There are massive differences in life expectancy at birth and equally large differences in the length of time people are ill before they die: their healthy life expectancy. The latest figures show very clearly the inequality in our society. Men in the most deprived areas of the country can expect to live 9.4 years less than those in the least deprived areas. For women the difference is 7.4 years. Men in the most deprived areas will spend on average 30 per cent of their shorter lives in ill health, about twice as much as men in the least deprived areas. Women can expect to live about 33 per cent of their lives in ill health, again about double those from the least deprived areas.

The appalling health gap revealed by these figures is far wider than for most comparable countries and has continued to grow in recent years. This means in very concrete terms that a woman in one of the most deprived areas of the UK will, on average, get her first significant long term illness at 47, whereas women from the most affluent areas will enjoy 20 more years of good health. Changing this will require a massive effort from many sectors over many years but we need to start now.

The All-Party Group published a strategy in early 2020 designed both to change the way older people are seen and to tackle these awful differences across the country. It calls for a cross-party consensus and, just like *Health is made at home*, it proposes concerted and complementary action from government, the NHS and wider society. Everyone has their part to play.

The Group's focus is on prevention rather than health creation but there is clear overlap between the two and, like other organisations described here, it calls for a wider social movement to promote health and wellbeing. This important work is another indication that people from different backgrounds and different starting points are converging around the same broad set of ideas, and that the timing is right for real change. And the Covid-19 pandemic appears to be accelerating the process.

We will return to all these ideas in the final chapters of the book.

***

Many of us will need care towards the end of our lives.

Much of this care will be provided by family members, particularly women. One in five people aged between 50 and 70 are regular care providers, an activity that limits their own ability to live life to the full and affects their own health.

Informal carers and voluntary organisations, as noted in Chapter 2, provide services that, if monetised, would amount to about the same value as the country spends on the NHS and social care – around £130 billion in 2019. The care provided is the equivalent of about 8 million professional care workers.

It's in the interests of the taxpayer, as well as all the millions of people involved in giving or receiving care, that these carers are well supported. And we need to rebuild communities and create the new community infrastructure that will support local activities. It's extraordinary, as noted earlier, that the Government took away a great deal of existing social and community support in the name of austerity while, at the same time, talking loosely about the Big Society.

Successive governments' failure to resolve the social care crisis over many years is critically important. The problems have been well rehearsed in public but still no action has been taken. Lack of financial support and facilities mean that thousands of people are stuck in hospitals yet don't need to be there – blocking beds that could be used for people requiring healthcare – and many thousands more are trapped in their own homes with little or no support. These problems are aggravated by the poor pay and conditions of so many of the carers: a largely forgotten and ignored part of the workforce.

Resolving this crisis, however hard politically, must now be a priority. Care homes have been very badly affected by the virus and seemingly used as an overflow for the NHS rather than being treated as important in their own right. It is typical of how the sector has been neglected over the years. There is nothing new in the way millions of people provide care voluntarily and join voluntary organisations. Traditions of care and service go back centuries, and William Beveridge wrote about voluntary action in the 1940s at the very same time as he was setting out plans for the NHS. But the way things are done, and the methods, principles and beliefs that guide action have changed and will continue to do so. There is less emphasis on charity, more on social justice, and more on the idea that involving people needing care in normal life – rather than creating special environments or even hiding them away – is good for them and good for us all. Human interaction is key and we all get something out of it.

The response to the Covid-19 pandemic is just another instance of the public's willingness to volunteer and get involved in something it sees as worthwhile – and something that brings our communities and nation together.

Another example is palliative care. The UK invented the modern version of palliative care in the 20th century, with Dame Cicely Saunders creating the first purpose built hospice, St Christopher's, in London in 1967. It is a prime example of someone outside the NHS and government taking control and making something happen.

The UK is now generally rated as the best place in the world to die because of the way hospices are so well integrated within hospital and community services and the extensive network of community based hospices. However, as Claire Morris, global advocacy director for the Worldwide Hospice Palliative Care Alliance, told me, there is a postcode lottery in access to palliative care with some areas, generally the more affluent, better served than others. It is perhaps an inevitable result of the way hospices have been established by voluntary organisations rather than as part of a national programme.

Claire explained to me that there is a long-running debate about independence. The UK has more than 220 hospices, about a quarter of which are for children. The adult hospices receive on average more than 30 per cent of their income from the NHS, while the children's ones receive about 17 per cent. The rest, in both cases, comes from fundraising. Most hospices want to keep their independence of the state and are fiercely proud of the 125,000 volunteers nationally who keep them going. However, there are continual issues of sustainability and good arguments for the NHS funding an essential package of care to support hospices across the country.

There is another much broader current debate about palliative care and death, much of it about changing attitudes and bringing greater awareness of pain control on the one hand and encouraging us all to talk about death and dying on the other. There has been a recent Lancet Commission on palliative care and there is a current one looking into 'the Value of Death'.

One of the themes of the debate is whether we have over-medicalised death, leaving it to the professionals and losing some of the human and spiritual elements. There are now programmes in the UK where members of the local community are involved in providing support alongside family and professionals. Frome in Somerset is developing its Compassionate Communities model of primary and end-of-life care, which builds on existing social relationships and community connections.

It is a powerful model, which has already improved health in the area. And Claire says these compassionate communities demonstrate the important, equal relationship between the community and health systems in providing care, including at the end of life. It is also about taking control for ourselves, not leaving it all to the professionals.

***

Much palliative care is now provided in the community but the design of hospices and other health buildings is very important in providing the best conditions for the patients and their families. An example is the network of Maggie's Centres around the country that provide support and information for cancer patients and their families. All the centres are designed to reflect Maggie Keswick Jencks's and her husband Charles's belief in the ability of buildings to uplift people.

Elsewhere, the Dementia Services Development Centre at Stirling University has for more than 25 years provided research insights and design solutions for people living with dementia, helping to make communities dementia friendly and influence policy. Its ideas are spreading. So, too, are the developing ideas and thinking of many architects, designers and planners, who are working on improving housing for older people.

This discussion takes us into design and the environment, topics that will be discussed in Chapter 9. But first, in the next chapter, we look at communities. Sir Michael Marmot's work has provided evidence that in order to reduce health inequalities in England, we need to improve community capital and reduce social isolation across the social gradient. The Frome model promotes the idea of building on what is already there. And, as Hazel Stuteley of C2 Connecting Communities argues in Chapter 5, communities know how to heal themselves.

Public Health England argues that we should place communities at the heart of public health in order to help reduce health inequalities, engage those most at risk of poor health, improve resilience and community support, and empower people to have a greater say in their lives and health.

The next chapter shows this in action. It reinforces the many powerful arguments about why we need to align our thinking on communities and health, wellbeing and place, as well as people and the built and natural environments.

***

This chapter has continued the underlying themes that early intervention and prevention are better than picking up the pieces later, that action is better for us all than passivity, and that being autonomous and making our own decisions are vital to our health. A healthy old age depends on physical and mental activity but also on having a social life, having a meaning in life, and being in control of your own life.

The big issue in this chapter is *the importance of having a meaning and purpose in life.* This is vital at all ages but especially in older age when work and family no longer provide the framework for our lives.

And for government, the most urgent issue is the importance of *introducing new policies on social care for the benefit of everyone who needs support.*

CHAPTER EIGHT

JOINING THE DOTS IN THE COMMUNITY

Bernadette Kelly and Shelley Butler were two of the original Peer Navigators. Local women with children at school, they had been appointed by housing association Bolton at Home to support its tenants on the Johnson Fold estate.

They told me what they had been doing and what they had achieved over the last 18 months in their jobs. It was impressive. And some of the outcomes were quite unexpected.

They explained that it was their job to connect local residents to services – the navigator part – and also to listen to them, understand their needs, and respond where they could. One of the things they had concentrated on was working with families on food poverty and they took me to visit a mother and children's group and a community pantry.

There were about ten mothers in one of the rooms in a neighbourhood centre and about twice as many children, all under five years of age and not yet at school. They were busy around a large table making things with Duplo, cutting out patterns and colouring paper. There were some part eaten slices of pizza, bits of tomato squashed on the table and the floor, children calling out and running around. It was all chaotic, happy and fun. I was soon fully occupied.

They showed me the pantry in the next room. Behind a locked door there were shelves of food and toiletries, washing powder, disposable nappies, tampons, the essentials. Even some fresh vegetables, I noticed, but mostly packaged and tinned items that would keep. This was a community pantry, they emphasised – the Storehouse Pantry, not a food bank. Everyone who wanted to use it paid a one-off subscription of £2.50 to be a member and were then entitled to have access to the stock.

It was typical of Bolton at Home, I realised later: this respect for the dignity of its residents. And there was another underlying principle. We may all need help of some sort at different times in our lives and if you are a member, you are entitled to it.

They also hold cookery classes here. Sometimes, as I learned later, they use vegetables grown on a local community project. And there is a women's arts group. A place for women to be creative, to talk and to just be with each other. There are other activities, too, such as a healthy lifestyles group, uniform swaps and a holiday club for kids.

Everything was part of the same philosophy of listening to what people wanted, following their lead and responding. It wasn't about doing things for people but helping them do things for themselves. And some of the help that people need can appear very little to the outside eye.

Bernadette and Shelley explained that lack of confidence was often a very important issue, as were stress and depression. So they had to spend quite a lot of time ringing or messaging each week to remind or encourage people to attend meetings. They might also pick them up or '*knock on*' as they passed their house on the way to a group session. And they were constantly trying to encourage them, build confidence, be a friend, or get to know the family.

Small things to distant health or social services or a housing authority. But very big things in reality.

I asked how the Peer Navigators preserved their own privacy or personal space when they were also residents on the same estate. It wasn't always easy, they said. They had to work sometimes to make sure they had proper professional boundaries. They had to make sure people understood they weren't always on duty. But, of course, they were still neighbours and friends.

And sometimes there were difficult ethical decisions about crimes and things they might hear about. But as they said: *'People only let you see what they let you see.'*

It turned out this was Bernadette's last day in the job. She had been appointed to a permanent post as a customer services assistant elsewhere in the organisation. She told me that she had benefitted enormously by working in the role, growing in confidence and learning new skills. But no one had expected other members of her family to benefit in the same way. There had been a ripple effect, she believed, and now her husband was about to be employed as well. And her children had made new friends. Unsurprisingly, some of her neighbours wanted to apply for her job.

Shelley meanwhile was planning to do a youth and community work degree after her contract finished in a month's time. And another of the first four Peer Navigators had already got a permanent job some time ago.

The appointment of Peer Navigators is a new venture for Bolton at Home. It was being trialled for 18 months with an external evaluation to follow. It will be very interesting to see from this evaluation what has changed in that time, not just in terms of activities but also whether there have been measurable changes in behaviours, health or other indices in the community in this relatively short period.

Regardless of the findings of the evaluation, the organisation has already decided that it is worth continuing and has appointed new Peer Navigators to take over from Bernadette and Shelley. They are also appointing others on some of their other estates. The increase in activities and the life-changing impact on the Peer Navigators themselves have been enough to convince them.

This was the first time that Bolton at Home had designed jobs specifically for some of its own tenants, yet it had soon realised that its constitution and rules prohibited it from restricting appointments to its tenants only. Some organisations might have stopped there and given up. Instead, however, the housing association asked Bolton Community

Voluntary Services to make the appointments on its behalf and manage them jointly. A small change with a big impact.

New NHS Alliance, which will be discussed in Chapter 14, calls small changes like this *'Trojan Mice'*. Indeed, the Alliance gave Bolton at Home its Trojan Mouse Award for 2018 in recognition of the Peer Navigators scheme. Appointing local people into these roles allowed the housing association to achieve so much more than it would have done by employing people with no connection to the area, which, of course, would have been the usual way of doing things.

We had earlier visited a new Men in Sheds project on the same estate, where I talked with a small group of men who were slowly turning a semi derelict piece of land between the houses into a place for growing vegetables, and for meeting and doing things in their shed. Except they didn't have a shed yet. Just a run-down lock-up garage where they kept a kettle and a few tools. There was a dismantled greenhouse leaning up against one side of the garage ready to be put back together, along with some wood and other useful bits and pieces.

Men in Sheds is just what it sounds like. A larger version of a typical garden shed where men can work on whatever they want and however they want to do it. The Bolton network now has five locations and a waiting list. It was set up because of concerns about social isolation among older men in Bolton and because of higher than average levels of poor mental health and suicide.

I suppose that a different housing association with different priorities might have used this spare land for building another house or two, rather than letting the men have it for free. I was later taken by members of Bolton at Home's Community Investment Team to visit another Men in Sheds project, longer established and on a larger plot that could easily have taken four or five houses. Here, at Willow Hey, they grew vegetables for communal use, held barbeques, and staged events. They invited others – including women and children – to share their facilities, which consisted of some old armchairs, as well as workbenches and a cooking area. You could relax here, talk, or work quietly on your own project, doing your own thing but being with others.

We sat down in the shed with six or seven men aged from about 45 upwards and listened to their stories. Some were retired, others unable to work through illness; one had fallen into a deep despair after the death of his wife, others had endured periods of mental illness. Everyone had their own story. All found camaraderie in the shed, and a sense of purpose and worth to the community. They had a reason to get up in the morning and somewhere to go.

The more I saw of Bolton at Home's activities, the more I was impressed, not just by what it achieved but also by the potential of bodies like this all over the country. And I knew that there were others doing similar things.

Bolton at Home had taken over the council's housing stock of 26,500 units and now had about 18,000 left after some tenants had exercised their right to buy. These were spread over 11 estates, including some of the most deprived in the area. This history means that, like other housing associations that took over council housing, it has a real sense of belonging, of being part of Bolton. The housing association is explicitly aware of its role as a so-called anchor organisation in the town and of its contribution to placemaking, ideas we will return to in the next chapter. It wanted to make Bolton a better place to live where, in its words, there are *'homes and neighbourhoods we can all be proud of'*.

It undertakes a wide range of activities: helping people into employment, tackling domestic violence and looking after the most vulnerable, as well as servicing its tenants and property, and building more units. I was interested to note that it has maintained an arts programme and employed arts development workers for more than 20 years. And it has spent almost £2 million in grants to 83 voluntary, community and social enterprise partners in the last year.

All of this adds up to a real focus on building the community, which is in marked contrast to the way that many communities have been neglected in recent years. I wondered how it managed to do this. How, at a time when public authorities and providers of all sorts were being squeezed, had Bolton at Home managed to find the capacity to pursue some of its own objectives as well as focusing on national priorities?

I asked Noel Sharpe, executive director of customer and place, about this and she told me that Bolton at Home justified it through the bottom line. This community investment impacted in all kinds of ways on how well it could operate as a business. Reduced vandalism, tenants better able to look after themselves, more employment, greater social activity, children growing up healthier. It was good for the business and the right thing to do.

Behind it all was personal passion and an explicit organisational commitment to achieving social value, defined by the UN as economic, social and environmental wellbeing. The Peer Navigators are part of Bolton at Home's Community Investment Team, a group from diverse backgrounds who clearly share a passion for the aims of the organisation and constantly develop new ideas and approaches.

Meeting them, I was struck by what a powerful contribution they were making to health and doing so in so many different ways. I asked Noel how well they worked with the NHS locally. When we met in Bolton in 2019, her answer was rather disappointing but very similar to things I had heard elsewhere: it wasn't a particularly strong relationship.

Bolton at Home employed someone to work on delayed discharges from hospitals, as well as employing a housing officer for older people. It was also part of a falls collaborative, helping older people avoid falls in their home. The NHS had withdrawn funding for two health development workers some years ago and, while people were friendly enough, there wasn't a real emphasis on working together. She suggested that the NHS was too busy with its own priorities, very focused on its patients, and didn't really understand what housing associations could offer.

I wasn't really very surprised. I chaired a review six years ago that looked at problems with admissions to adult mental health units. We found that one of the biggest issues was housing. There wasn't enough suitable housing for people to live in the community while being treated, or for people to move to when ready for discharge. And the NHS, with rare exceptions, wasn't working with the local housing bodies. It didn't sound as if things had got any better.

In May 2020, however, Noel told me that things had moved on. She had been invited to be a member of the Integrated Care Partnership. She saw this as an opportunity to raise the profile of housing and the role it can play in improving health, tackling health inequalities and promoting the shift towards prevention. Housing organisations are being involved properly in the recovery planning.

It was similar to things I had been hearing elsewhere. Covid-19 was leading to improved working between different organisations, all of them focusing on the same issues. One of the big questions for the future is how these improvements can be held on to in the future.

I left Bolton with a great deal to think about. There were big themes here of localness, place, community, connection and belonging, which are obviously very important to people. And, writing this after the 2019 general election, they appear to be themes that have helped change politics locally with the Conservatives making big inroads into this traditional Labour territory.

I could also hear the echo of Africa's community health workers in the Peer Navigators – local women serving their neighbours and community. And I was reminded, too, of the founder of BRAC in Bangladesh when he said that the key thing was to *'empower the women'*. There were some of the same principles being applied here.

***

Later that evening, my wife Siân and I were in Salford meeting another group of people who were changing their communities for the better. There was a lifesize figure of the artist LS Lowry sitting on a stool at the bar just behind us. It was a pub where he used to drink and it looked as if he might turn around any moment and join the discussion.

This time it was all about empowering the men.

One of the members of the group, John Horrocks, said *'the GP couldn't cure me but the community could'*.

He had been agoraphobic for years and had undergone eight sessions of treatment, he told us. But none of it had lasting effect and he couldn't manage to remain at work.

Now it was different. *'And it was partly knowing that there were other people out there feeling the same way,'* he said.

Heather Henry met John when she was employed as a project worker to help improve the health of people on an estate in Salford. She is a nurse but wasn't employed as one and her approach was deliberately non-clinical. She focused on strengths – *'what's strong, not what's wrong'* – and on building on whatever local resources and capabilities were present.

Her employer, Chris Dabbs, had realised that the local fathers, many unemployed or unable to work, some separated from their partners and some largely absent from their children's lives, were a vital unused resource. And there was so much they could do with a bit of initial encouragement and support.

Chris managed to secure funding from the NHS and the result was Salford Dadz Little Hulton – a group, led by the men themselves, which now runs many activities on the estate and has demonstrated improvements in the health and wellbeing of not only the men themselves but also their children. And, just as happened in Bolton, it has improved life for others on the estate.

It took time, of course, and perseverance. John told us how positive it was to be treated as a person and a father, not a patient, but how hard some of the things were for him to do. He became a volunteer with the group in 2015 and the first time he went to a board meeting of the sponsoring body, he travelled eight miles to get there, the farthest he had been from home in ten years.

At other times he was so anxious that he couldn't think straight or read anything. And, he said, the help he and his family were given by the NHS sometimes just disabled him further, turning him back into a helpless patient. But after two years of employment in what he called his *'community cure'*, John has now moved on, taking a health and social care diploma and getting a job with the ambulance service. Some of the other Dadz have also got jobs or moved on in their lives.

John and some of the other men have now spoken at lots of meetings and events, but Heather said that in the beginning, she was only 50 per cent certain that they would even turn up. Thankfully, they did. And, as she said, it was extraordinarily powerful when John spoke about his emotional problems as a man. It gave him such a power to connect with people and to help people understand the problems – and the possibilities.

Heather told us how on one occasion a police officer, who was also a local father, stood up and talked about his feelings after one of the Dadz had spoken in a community meeting. *'His wife's jaw dropped open. She had never seen him talk like that. When the first dad shared his feelings, it opened up a floodgate for other fathers who realised that they weren't alone with their feelings. Then they bonded and helped each other and that's how they healed.'*

Heather's approach involved listening to what local people see as the problems and what they see as the solutions. She repeated something Hazel Stuteley had said about the TR14ers in Camborne: *'Communities know how to cure themselves if they are given the chance.'*

I asked Heather about her role as a professional. It was quite subtle, she explained. *'You start at the front of the room and gradually move towards the back.'*

Sometimes, she said, *'you have to be deliberately helpless and let them work out their own solutions'.*

It was about creating and using a network and building relationships with other people and organisations that might be able to help. And helping other professionals to change their approaches. Power, as she explained, isn't a zero sum game. *'But you do need to flip the power balance, change the language you use and see the world differently.'*

She didn't need to be a nurse to be the project manager, she told us, although it helped her with some insights. Others could bring different skills and understanding to the role. The one time it had really been useful was when she was told by local women that they weren't worried about her because she was a professional. Therefore, they said, she wouldn't be having an affair with any of the men with whom she spent so such time. And she knew they would also be aware that she would be interested in child protection and would notice problems.

Chris Dabbs was the other person around the table that evening. He is the chief executive of Unlimited Potential, a Salford based community benefit society that aims to help *'people to fulfil all of their rich potential and lead healthier and happier lives'.* It runs a whole range of interesting and innovative projects, from tackling obesity and asthma to support for carers and healthy living. The common thread is that projects are all designed to enable people and communities to use their strengths and assets in new and positive ways.

Heather stressed that it was Chris's vision that had led Unlimited Potential to set up the project that eventually became Salford Dadz using NHS funding as well as through some charitable funds, and it has had two more projects in Salford and Rochdale under the title *Dadly Does it.*

Both Chris and Heather pointed out that money wasn't always the main issue – but gaining influence was key. They pointed me to Wigan, which had suffered the largest cuts in grant of any local authority. It had worked with all the local organisations to create the Wigan Deal, which looked at needs in the round and funded local initiatives that used the strengths and assets of local people.

You need to look at all the resources of a community, all the hidden strengths, all the services, and the commercial organisations. *'What's the role of Morrisons?'* Chris asked. *'What about hairdressers, the chippy?*

'What about asking supermarkets to help identify malnutrition among older people? 'And young people to help older people use apps?'

It is all about identifying needs and looking at who can help. And strength comes from finding internal solutions.

Chris Dabbs, Heather Henry, John Horrocks and others are all engaged in spreading these messages locally, building links with the much larger Greater Manchester authorities and groups. There is increasing recognition of the importance of enabling men to share their emotions and engage with others. It is also about ensuring that fathers are engaged in family policy and included by the professionals in discussions about their children and family. And, of course, the men can play a vital role in supporting each other in all aspects of health and wellbeing including suicide prevention.

They told me that the learning from Salford Dadz and Dadly Does It has been recognised by the inclusion of 'positive fatherhood' in plans in Salford, Rochdale and Greater Manchester. It is surely only the beginning.

Their work is a strong reminder of the themes of this book that everyone has a role to play in improving health, and that we need to take back control of our health and communities.

I wondered what Lowry would have said if he had leaned across and joined in. He was every inch a local artist and innovator. And he can still make us see the world differently.

***

I heard about Incredible Edible from several different people. It sounded like an intriguing idea – growing food in public spaces, odd bits of land in a town, on roundabouts, outside public buildings, alongside the road. It seemed to be a mix of community gardening and healthy eating. When I met the founder, Pam Warhurst, she told me that it was really a Trojan horse. Not a mouse in this case, but something much bigger and more public.

'Food,' she said, 'was just the entry point. Everyone likes food so it's a way of bringing people together.' Her aim, she told me, was 'to create kind, confident, connected communities'.

It became clear as we talked that this wasn't just a nice soft idea but something much more radical and grittier. She wants to change the way the NHS and government work, and boost the local economies in towns, estates and boroughs around the country. Her ambitions are much bigger. 'The whole point,' she told me, 'is to create a new normal in how we live.'

Pam had conceived the idea 11 years ago, when discussing with some friends what they could do to improve their community of Todmorden, a small town in the Pennines just west of Leeds. They were all concerned about climate change and about what they could do. Food was a way of bringing people together and growing it drew attention to the environment. The idea has since spread around the country with more than 150 groups already engaged.

I met Pam with her colleague Gary Stott to discuss their work. They told me that the organisation's activities are centred around three plates. A community plate, which is about bringing people together; a learning plate, which is about food and healthy eating; and a business plate, which is about creating jobs.

The community is the starting point. Pam describes planting in public areas as creating *'propaganda gardens'*, places that draw attention and start conversations. They make people think, as well as providing healthy activity and companionship.

The gardens really are a Trojan horse.

Then comes the learning plate: learning from each other and other groups. Learning from older people about things like pickling, and from refugees about their plants and food. Gary also works with Community Shop CiC, the UK's first social supermarket chain, and he described how some projects had branched out into selling the produce. West Norwood, he told me, not only has several community gardens but also a community shop, and every two months it holds a community feast, sharing the profits and the produce.

The business plate is also, in part, about learning. It is about creating jobs for the future and supporting the local economy. Food is big business and can be produced locally, chefs can be trained and local food outlets opened. And they can be healthier than the endless multiples selling junk food in so many of our streets. Incredible Edible is also encouraging business to create apprenticeships for local people, and they are having some success in places as far apart as Middlesbrough and Bristol.

Each local project plans its activities around these three plates and is connected by a team of regional facilitators who encourage shared learning. Incredible Edible is building a movement for change which, like others described in this book, is vision led rather than prescriptive, with each group autonomous and self-directing. A quick scroll through the website reveals the extraordinary diversity of the groups involved. People from all different backgrounds and coming at it from different perspectives. Some are clearly nature lovers and born gardeners, others are active climate warriors and community activists, while others are just enjoying themselves and their communities.

The movement is all about health and wellbeing, together with community spirit, self-belief and confidence. It is also about fun and a bit of showbiz as well. In-your-face planting in public space – *'propaganda gardens'*.

To be truly successful, Incredible Edible needs to change what happens in the boardrooms of local authorities, NHS trusts, and other public and private bodies. Pam has been a metropolitan council leader and was the chair of Calderdale NHS Trust, so she knows her way around these boardrooms and is beginning to be consulted about national policy.

She argues that Incredible Edible helps combat loneliness, is part of the growing movement of social prescribing, and that NHS estates departments should be investing in community kitchens. And she believes the NHS should be using its procurement policy to support local communities as part of the circular economy – where people buy local produce, keeping the money in the local community.

Local groups also need access to land – and that's proving difficult. Public land, common land really, to be used by the people of the area. I wonder how radical elected members and officials are willing to be in supporting these local enterprises.

'I know people can do things differently,' Pam said, referring to the officials and the authorities.

Some of them get it, she told me, and Incredible Edible is welcomed in some communities. *'It needs to be top down and bottom up,'* she said. *'You can't have just one party. We need both hands to clap.'*

They need help from people like Pam and Incredible Edible to learn what they can do. It is a neat reversal of the normal government approach where the professionals and officials tell people what to do to be healthy.

***

It is too easy to think of these sorts of community health projects as rehabilitation, helping people to recover or as just patching up a failing system. There is something absolutely fundamental here, something much more strategic, which needs to become mainstream in our whole approach to health and wellbeing.

It's the point really that Harry Burns made in talking about young children and the Scottish Early Years Initiative. Our focus needs to be on healthy children and healthy people in a healthy and stable community. You can't have one without the other.

The estates in Bolton and Salford, described earlier, are officially classified as deprived. There are real problems of poverty, lack of education, exclusion, low status, and lack of power. And all of them exemplified in the North by years of industrial decline and political neglect. Yet, as we have seen, there is also strength and hope.

There needs to be political action and investment, and it needs to be sustained and not short term or linked to one political cycle. But that won't be enough by itself. As these and other accounts tell us, salvation isn't going to come purely from outside with things being done to and for these communities. They need to build it themselves and base it on their own internal strengths.

I have talked about this over the years with Lord Andrew Mawson. He is a serial social entrepreneur from Bradford who arrived in the early 1980s as a young minister in Bromley-by-Bow, in East London, to find himself with a large church and a small congregation.

At first, he was unsure what he was going to do but he soon found out. The church started being used by a nursery. Then a young woman started a small business running dance classes. Bengali women needed somewhere to meet. And so it went on. Eventually, and after a struggle with the authorities, the Bromley by Bow Centre was born. It is a pioneering charity that combines an extensive neighbourhood hub with a medical practice, local businesses and a community research project.

Andrew has gone on to be involved in the Docklands redevelopment, the Olympic Park legacy, and in redeveloping a street, St Paul's Way in Mile End, so that the schools, local businesses, housing association, local surgery, NHS and voluntary organisations are all working together to improve the area. Aspirations are high. University College London is involved, a pharma company is carrying out research on diabetes with local sixth formers, there is a science summer school run with Professor Brian Cox, and the first young people have gone on to Oxbridge.

Andrew calls it *'joining the dots'*. It involves bringing people and organisations together around the common needs and problems of the area. The private sector, the public sector, the university sector, and the not for profit sector. They don't need to agree on politics but they do need some shared vision and values, and to be entrepreneurial. Most significantly of all, they need to create the all important relationships that, in the end, are what help to get things done.

Andrew now leads Well North Enterprises, a community interest company that works with towns and cities to create healthy and thriving environments for the future. This and the Bromley by Bow Centre are discussed further in Chapter 14.

***

These community based organisations have all been particularly active during the pandemic in supporting their communities in various ways. Some of their activities are described in the round up of activity in Chapter 16.

The big idea in this chapter is *to connect and communicate*. Most of the success stories in this book depend on people making connections between ideas and between people and organisations. Much of this is simply about bringing people together to create a sense of solidarity and shared interest, and to spark ideas and develop creative solutions. It is also about combatting isolation and loneliness, and breaking down the barriers, real and imagined, that separate people.

The discussion in this chapter has been all about geographical communities, places where people live and meet each other. Many of the same considerations apply to other sorts of communities based, for example, on interests, sexuality, beliefs or ethnicity – any group that also gives people a sense of belonging and identity. These are discussed further in Chapter 11.

CHAPTER NINE

DESIGN AND THE ENVIRONMENT

This chapter offers a different perspective on communities by looking at the importance of design, planning and the natural environment. It begins with two communities that nobody wants to join: patients in hospital with long term spinal injuries, and people in prisons and detention centres. Both are very stressful environments.

There are some wonderful examples of life-enhancing developments in the UK and a great tradition to draw on going back two centuries and more. Today, the positive impact that both the built and natural environments can have on health and wellbeing is becoming increasingly well known. This is not the whole story, however, and there is a danger that in some places, standards have slipped dramatically and we may well be creating new 21st century slums.

The Covid-19 lockdown has shown us how important our homes and the quality of the built environment is to our overall health, and our mental wellbeing in particular. We must make sure we learn from the experience and press government to set minimum standards regarding size, access to daylight and other beneficial design features.

Architects, designers, planners and their clients all have an enormous part to play in creating health and wellbeing. We need the political will to ensure that they can do so.

***

There needed to be a garden, Horatio Chapple and his father David decided, some outdoor space where patients could go with their families and friends. Patients had to be able to get off the ward sometimes.

Horatio was working at the time as a volunteer on the Duke of Cornwall Spinal Treatment Centre in Salisbury Hospital, where his father was one of the surgeons. As his mother, Dr Olivia Chapple, later told me, Horatio was young and saw things with fresh eyes, refusing to just accept what older people had learned to tolerate. He wanted to change things.

That summer, he conducted a survey to find out what patients thought was needed and to help him argue the case for creating a garden for the ward. The results showed the patients wanted a garden for relaxation. They saw its potential to be a beautiful and peaceful place. Outside the Treatment Centre, a little piece of normality, an escape from hospital life. Later, after his death at the age of just 17, his parents decided they would build the garden in his memory.

Unlike the patients, many of the hospital staff saw a garden as a wonderful opportunity to do more clinically. It could be a place for extra therapy, an extension of the ward where there would be scope to carry out different sorts of exercises and treatments. They could use the full range of their skills for the benefit of their patients.

There had been much discussion but, in the end, as Olivia told me, they had followed through the findings of Horatio's original survey. It would be an antidote to the therapy, an escape from the clinical areas. The patients knew what they needed. It was the space that mattered, a space where they could be themselves away from all the burdensome routines.

I met Olivia in Horatio's Garden in Salisbury. She had been a GP but gave up her practice when Horatio died in order to concentrate on developing the garden, which she now ran. It was a pretty summer's day and the garden was alive with colour. It sits on the edge of the hospital, partially overlooked from above but with a sense of privacy and space. I had come in from the hospital car park and couldn't see the garden until I was inside. Once there, my eyes were drawn to the planting all around me and the acres of sky above. And the view over the boundary hedge and out over the Wiltshire countryside, adding to the impression of space.

The garden has a number of beds of different sizes and shapes, some raised, mostly filled with flowers and shrubs but with a space for vegetables and a few fruit trees. A large bed at the centre of the main area of the garden has a path around it. It has been planted with some taller shrubs and flowers, so you can't see across it if you're in a wheelchair or sitting in one of the chairs dotted around. It creates lots of spaces for private conversations or for being alone.

There's a greenhouse large enough for wheelchairs and with potting tables at the right level. At the farthest end of the garden is a small glass-fronted room, where you can be totally private if you want and still enjoy a view of the garden. There's also a conservatory, which acts as a reception area and cafe with a few tables and chairs, and lots of space for wheelchairs or beds. Patients and their families can use it to meet when it's raining or to come and make a hot drink or something to eat.

I realised while talking to Olivia just how carefully this had all been designed; every detail had been thought through, every detail mattered. The designer, Cleve West, had spent hours with patients, families and staff. The Treatment Centre is the only part of the hospital where patients are here for a long time – many months, even years – and many come back time and again over the years. The space really mattered, Olivia told me. Space to be with family and friends, it helped keep people together, she said. *'And it has changed the balance of power,'* she added. *'The patients are the hosts.'*

Olivia explained to me that whether or not a patient's rehabilitation is successful in the long term is very dependent on their psychological state. What keep a patient going, she said, are family and friends, and some sense of normality. Connections with their past life but also with their future, people who would be there when they left hospital. But loneliness was an issue, she said. And young people whose lives had been changed by their injury needed to learn a new personal narrative and practice it with volunteers as they reinvented themselves. The calm of the garden was an ideal place to talk in private.

The garden was used by people in different ways. I saw one patient come down in a bed accompanied by a member of staff, another in a wheelchair pushed by his mother. A man in a wheelchair came to make tea in the reception area. A nurse from another part of the hospital ate a sandwich for lunch while sitting on a chair by the central bed, the large pinkish purple flowers of Cleome swaying beside her. Bees foraged in the lavender. Everyone was welcome.

There were organised activities too: the hospital's artist in residence gave classes here. Some people planned the year's crops and potted up seedlings, but most did their own thing. Therapy, but not therapy. It was not the endless and repetitive routines of strengthening muscles, and helping damaged bodies and brains learn new movements.

David Chapple, Horatio's father, joined us during a break from surgery. He and Olivia told me a bit about how difficult it had been to make all this happen, even for them as NHS insiders with the goodwill of their colleagues and the hospital trust. A hospital is simply not geared to this sort of thing, the focus is totally clinical.

There were many barriers to progress. Approvals were needed, access to services, engineering assessments, insurances: all the important details that would ensure the project's long term sustainability. And the Chapples needed to fundraise, engage a designer and plan the garden. In the end, though, they won, and the garden was up and running very quickly once all the approvals and inspections were complete.

The feedback from patients and their families has been tremendous, very positive and liberating. Clinical staff, too, value the garden and, among other things, have noticed that some patients are much calmer and there has been a reduction in challenging behaviours.

The Chapples have gone on to commission other gardens in other spinal units. There are now six altogether, with Horatio's Gardens in Edinburgh and Cardiff, as well as others in England. Each of them different, each purpose designed for the site, and each created with the involvement of patients, families and staff.

This is a story about vision and determination, and about something life-enhancing coming out of a tragedy. It is also an account of how careful design of the physical environment, with the full engagement of users, can be healing and improve health and wellbeing.

***

Chris Liddle adopted a similar user based approach when HLM Architects was chosen to design a new immigrant removal centre at one of the UK's airports even though, of course, the aims of the development were very different. The task he faced was how to ensure the safety of everyone in the facility, make sure it was secure and, at the same time, reduce stress levels.

Over the years, Chris and his colleagues have developed considerable expertise in designing for stressful environments. They have designed prisons and a young offenders' institution, always very conscious of the people for whom they were designing. They have also designed hospitals, schools and defence establishments. They don't have a house architectural style, they say, because they work with their clients and seek to shape their buildings and spaces around the needs of the people who use them.

Chris told me it's important to start with the staff. The rhetoric in the NHS, he said, is always patients first. And he could understand that, but it is important to look after your people. They are key to de-stressing the situation and creating a safe and healthy environment. If staff are confident, calm and secure, they will be better able to look after patients, or manage prisoners or detainees effectively. Everyone will be safer.

It's an important point, reinforced for us all today by the importance of looking after NHS and care staff during the Covid-19 pandemic, making sure that they have the protective equipment they need and that their families are looked after while they are at work. We need them to give of their best and not be distracted by concerns about personal safety or the welfare of their family.

The detention centre is a very large and complex development. It will accommodate more than 1000 people of many different nationalities, some of whom will have to be kept apart from each other at all times. It's stressful for all of them, as they are all being removed from the country. The anxiety mounts as they near the point of departure, with some people attempting to injure themselves in order that they will be taken to hospital, or even trying to kill themselves. Safety for everyone is vital and so is security. The centre won't be a prison, but security will be equivalent to a Category B prison like Wormwood Scrubs with, for example, 7.6 metre external walls.

Chris told me that you have to *'walk the walk'* when you are designing an environment. Plan out and follow a day in the life of staff and inmates. It's the fourth dimension of the architects' drawing, he said. What's happening at different times, who is where, and what they see and experience. And then you try to shape the experience positively, to influence the person's mood and expectations. There is an established set of ideas that can help: long views for example, daylight, seeing greenery, colour schemes. And pictures and drawings that evoke memory or emotions. All can contribute to reducing stress and, in the right circumstances, promoting health and wellbeing.

It's all about people ultimately. Understanding the situation and the circumstances, and how people will experience the buildings and spaces you provide. It's also about people and communities. Even in prisons, Chris explained, you try to create some sense of community, spaces for safe interaction and anything that offers a connection back to the outside world.

I had earlier visited with Chris a school campus in Plymouth, which demonstrated this idea of community very clearly. It combined a senior school with a primary school and a special school. There were common areas but each school also had its own space. They had put the special school right next to the main entrance, so that the children weren't hidden away but were very obviously part of the whole community.

***

The two rather extreme examples of patients in a spinal injuries unit and people incarcerated in prisons and detention centres illustrate the importance of design, and show something of what can be done to improve health and wellbeing even in these difficult circumstances.

Design, of course, is never the only criterion in development, and health and wellbeing are not the only design considerations. Finance, different perspectives, culture and history are all important, but good design can take all these into account. And the UK has an extraordinary wealth of experience and creativity, which can be used to great effect – drawing both on the technical experts and on the experts by experience, the people who will live with the consequences of poor design and bad policy.

The challenge is enormous with the provision of better designed housing for older people being the single biggest element. A national network of older activists, the Older People's Housing Champions, is working to raise awareness of the impact of poor and unsuitable housing on older people's health and wellbeing, and press for improvements.

A few figures from their analysis, *Housing Action for Ageing Well*, demonstrate the scale of the issue. Ninety-six per cent of older households live in mainstream housing, while 80 per cent say they want to stay there. Two million older households live in poor housing conditions, with only 7 per cent of all homes accessible to people with disabilities.

It is no surprise that the estimated cost of poor housing for the NHS is £1.4 billion each year. Sixty-one per cent of this is due to excess cold, 31 per cent due to falls at home, 2 per cent from fires, and the remaining 6 per cent from different causes. Much of this is preventable.

The Independent Living Strategy Group is another group of people who are pressing for fundamental change. Independent living, as they say in a recent position statement, means disabled people living in the community with the same choices, control and freedom as any other citizen. '*Independent living is what non-disabled people take for granted,*' they say.

Disabled people want to be in control and for any practical assistance to be based on their own choices and aspirations. It is not just about social care and support services but about removing the barriers that stop them playing a full part in their communities. In their powerful statement, they argue that we all want a society that includes everyone, and that we all benefit from living in inclusive, accessible and welcoming communities. It is about taking back control for themselves and for their communities.

There have been major improvements over the last 30 years or so but, as the Group's chair, Baroness Jane Campbell, told me, a great deal has been lost in the last few years – with cuts in support meaning people are becoming more dependent again, and disabled people remaining on the periphery of decision making. It is, as Jane pointed out, more expensive to make people dependent as well as being bad for their health and welfare.

The Group's calls for greater engagement are only being answered in a very few cases. Hammersmith and Fulham Council, for example, set up a Disabled Peoples Commission and has committed itself to long term partnership in developing services and the community. It is an approach that will serve the local people and the Council well in future years.

I discussed these and other developments with Jeremy Porteus. He is the chief executive of the Housing Learning and Improvement Network, a network and repository of good practice and research on housing. He has played a major role in linking housing, health and social care in recent years, and wrote several of the '*Housing our Ageing Population: Panel for Innovation*' (HAPPI) reports, which set out the essential design principles in housing for older people. He, like others, has drawn attention to the fact that what is good for older people will also be good for the NHS.

I asked Jeremy to point me in the direction of good recent developments that promote health and wellbeing. He told me about Ebbsfleet Garden City: one of the ten Healthy New Towns being developed with guidance and support from NHS England and Public Health England. Each of these is being designed to create not only new homes but also a vibrant and cohesive place where people will want to live and work.

Central to all the Healthy New Towns is the concept of placemaking, a term used in different ways by different people. At its core is the idea of focusing on a local community's assets, inspiration and potential, with the intention of creating a community and public spaces that promote people's health, happiness and wellbeing. To quote the Danish architect Jan Gehl: '*First life, then spaces, then buildings – the other way around never works.*'

Ebbsfleet was already being developed before it was designated a Healthy New Town, so some of the ideas had to be retrofitted. One early development, however, appears to be showing real progress. A study that looked at quality of life and social sustainability – the way that the physical environment relates to how people live in and use the space, and function as a community – has produced positive results. It is undoubtedly an improvement on the Ferrier Estate, a bleak post-war housing development in Kidbrooke, Greenwich with serious social issues.

Jeremy also introduced me to a firm of architects that had designed a smaller housing estate in another part of the country, which would have a good social mix and was designed to enhance the residents' health and wellbeing. I was on my way to see it when the lead architect rang. The developer had decided to change the plans in ways that destroyed the community ethos. It was a straightforward commercial decision and the architects felt it went against all their principles. They had, with great sadness, resigned from the project.

These two examples reveal something of today's contrary trends in development and planning.

***

The UK has a tremendous historical tradition of designing towns and cities that support people to live happy, healthy and fulfilled lives. Port Sunlight, New Lanark and Bournville Village were all created by pioneering industrialists, while the garden cities developed from the ideas of John Ruskin, William Morris and others in the Arts and Crafts movement with their utopian vision of a better society.

The Town and Country Planning Association (TCPA) was founded in 1899 and brought together ideas of social justice, beauty in design, health and wellbeing, and economic efficiency. It shaped and led the development of Letchworth and, later, Welwyn Garden City as places that were '*designed for healthy living and industry of a size that makes possible a full measure of social life but not larger, surrounded by a rural belt; the whole of the land being in public ownership, or held in trust for the community*'.

The founders recognised the intrinsic value of beauty in design and in the natural environment to people's health and wellbeing. And today, the TCPA explicitly sees planning as a creative artistic activity, as well as a technical and analytical subject.

I talked with Hugh Ellis, policy director of the TCPA, about the current state of UK planning and housing. It is a very mixed picture. He confirmed my impression that there was enormous creativity and talent in the whole field of design and planning and, he stressed, there was very good evidence of what worked and what didn't. Yet, as a major review on reforming the English planning system, the Raynsford Review of Planning, spelled out, there is a real danger that we are creating 21st century slums.

The review concluded that *'deregulation had weakened the planning process to such an extent that some local authorities had little control over their own urban environment'*. There is an argument that the market will provide what is needed. But not if the market fails. People will live in poor housing if that is all that is on offer. Homeless families will accept rented accommodation of whatever standard. They don't have a choice. And it can do them and our society harm.

Hugh explained to me that both building and design regulations had been relaxed, so there were no minimum standards, only a menu of options. The result is that there are some very shoddy buildings being built. Worse still are some office conversions where people are expected to live in rooms without windows. The size of rooms and houses are often much smaller than the Parker Morris standards that applied from 1919 to 1980. As the Raynsford Review concluded: *'No system can be judged as 'working' if it cannot secure basic standards of light, space or places for children to play.'*

Public health and the need for healthy housing were two of the original drivers for creating a planning process. And for years, both planning and housing were the responsibility of the health minister, with planners educated on public health matters. But, as Hugh explained to me, planning became a much narrower discipline after the Second World War, partly in response to the failure of many post-war slum clearance and high-rise schemes. Planning by then had acquired a bad reputation.

Today, planners don't need to know anything about public health, Hugh told me. But, he added, doctors are now being educated about housing and social provision. And Sir Michael Marmot spelled out the importance of housing to health in the ten-year update of his *Marmot Review: Fair Society, Healthy Lives.* Health, it seems, is ready to reclaim the territory.

The TCPA is proposing that Parliament should pass a Healthy Homes Bill to address these problems. It would be designed to ensure the development of decent homes, which enhance, rather than undermine, people's health, safety and wellbeing.

The draft Bill contains ten high-level principles, which are worth listing. *Homes must be safe in relation to the risk of fire. Have adequate living space. Have access to natural light. Be accessible, and located in an environment that is also accessible as well as safe. Be within walkable neighbourhoods. Secure radical reductions in carbon emissions in line with the provisions of the Climate Change Act 2008. Have walkable access to green and play space that is open to everyone. Be resilient to a changing climate. Be secure and meet standards that design out crime. And meet enhanced standards to prevent unacceptable noise pollution.*

The Bill is a manifesto for change. It's hardly utopian but it is ambitious in scale and built on good evidence. It's all practical common sense. And, the experience of lockdown has shown us just how important our home environments are to our health and mental wellbeing.

Institutions will need to change, too, with more devolution and local decision making. Lord Michael Heseltine, the former deputy prime minister, has recently published his proposals for *Empowering English Cities.* He believes that we need to redesign our administrative structures and create new institutions that are fit for the future, with more power devolved to mayors and local authorities. His rallying cry at the end of his report is very relevant to the central themes of this book: *'Perversely, as global forces present challenges unimaginable to earlier generations, it is to the empowerment of people as individuals that we must look for a response. Global power must be challenged by little battalions. Individuals leading great companies, public servants of shining dedication, communities embracing the weak as well as the strong, cities proud of and exploiting their strengths. Each of us in it together.'*

Looking globally, there is a great deal of interest in healthy cities and the building up of evidence about their impact on health and wellbeing, sustainability, efficiency, social justice and prosperity. Very similar ideas to the utopian visions of the past.

SALUS, the publisher of *Health is made at home*, is one of the leaders in this field bringing together researchers, practitioners and policy thinkers in a global knowledge exchange around how we design systems, services and environments to support human and planetary health.

As Marc Sansom, SALUS's founding director, told me, the concept and ideal of healthy cities are gaining traction but are *'still falling down the gaps between silos'*. He believes, however, that *'the pandemic may finally bring about more joined-up, collaborative thinking across the public and private sectors and the community, with recognition that the health of the city is only as resilient as its healthcare system, and our healthcare system is only as resilient as the city or community it serves'*.

Successful change requires vision and ideas about what works, political will to make change happen, and a means for successful delivery. The vision and ideas are there, but we need the political will and delivery through the market and other mechanisms.

***

The natural environment is integral to good design for health, whether through using natural light or greenery. Examples in earlier chapters illustrate this: from forest schools and Path Hill Farm's work with excluded children, to Incredible Edible in the last chapter or Horatio's Garden in this. These are only the tip of the iceberg with many more examples, ranging from the important work in recent years of the Royal Horticultural Society on health, to the growing popularity of community gardens and the introduction of living walls and green roofs. And Covid-19 has led to more people enjoying gardening and recognising the benefits, as described in Chapter 16.

And there is plenty of evidence and science behind it. Health textbooks now illustrate the positive impact of the natural world on the brain and physiology, as well as on mood and mental health. And, of course, trees and greenery play a vital role in absorbing air pollution in our towns and reducing carbon dioxide levels.

There is a wider picture here, too, that embraces the future of farming, air pollution, sustainability and planetary health. These are discussed in the next chapter, Chapter 10.

***

The big idea here is that *the environment matters*. Both the built and the natural environment profoundly affect our health and wellbeing. Whether you are incarcerated in a prison or a removal centre, stuck in a hospital bed, or living life to the full in your own home and neighbourhood.

The Covid-19 lockdown has demonstrated the importance of the environment for us all and has revealed the enormous differences in the quality of homes and neighbourhoods. People in lockdown with big gardens and large rooms in the leafy suburbs or the countryside have had a very different experience from people living in small flats with limited space, natural light and access to the outside world.

For government, the key proposal here is to *support the Healthy Homes Bill and provide the political will to deliver the improvements in housing and planning that are so urgently needed.*

CHAPTER TEN
SUSTAINABILITY AND PLANETARY HEALTH

Sourcing goods locally has been growing in popularity for some time, well before the pandemic exposed the risks in our global supply chains.

What things do we want to be dependent on other countries for in the future? Will we still want to get our February strawberries from Ecuador, our year-round roses from Kenya and all manner of manufactured goods from China? And what about vaccines, drugs and personal protective equipment?

Even more profoundly, what about care workers to look after disabled and elderly people, and farm workers to pick and pack crops? What will be the effect on our workforce and our economy? And what, of course, will be the impact on other poorer countries if we don't rely on their products, people and services?

It seems reasonable to suppose that there will be a significant change in how countries supply themselves with goods and physical commodities in future, but this is likely to be accompanied by an enormous increase in services and information delivered virtually. In other words, there will simultaneously be a retreat towards local production on the one hand and an increase in global connectedness on the other. Globalisation continuing but taking a different form.

Peter Kingsley of the Oracle Partnership suggests that the virus is accelerating changes already underway. He writes: *'On the near horizon … AI, remote robotics, computer controlled local manufacturing and supply networks will begin to deliver widespread benefits. The world is set to be dominated by virtual services, not simply physical goods. Picture a future where everyone can license an idea from anywhere in the world and begin production to meet local needs. Remote 3D manufacturing may lead to 'App store' markets for designs, so that pretty well anything can be fabricated around the corner, or at home, including food. The best may be adapted from around the world to meet local needs. A world of virtual manufacturing and remote services …'*

This idea of local production and global connections fits very naturally with many of the people and organisations described in this book. Some are explicitly seeking to source goods locally and build up local economies, recognising that poverty is the source of many of the problems they are tackling. Local authorities have, of course, traditionally promoted their communities in this way. Some authorities are now going further by linking this with action on recycling and environmental concerns, and attempting to create a circular economy where waste products are reused in different ways.

Some are explicitly allying themselves with the environmental movement, most recently represented by Extinction Rebellion and its nationwide and global protests. In declaring a climate emergency, the UK and other governments have given extra weight to the demands of environmental activists. And there has been further impetus in the UK through its hosting of the UN Climate Change Summit, originally scheduled for Glasgow in 2020 prior to the pandemic but now moved to 2021.

A great deal has already been written about the positive impact of lockdowns. Some of this has focused on how reducing production, energy use and traffic around the world has been good for the environment, with much less pollution and a reduction in the emissions that cause global warming. There are also signs that people are changing their lifestyles permanently. More homeworking may help revive local communities and reduce travel to work. It may also contribute to long term reductions in global air traffic. And, if the Government gets its way, social distancing on public transport will encourage us to cycle or walk to work.

And, in the short to medium term at least, we will take our holidays locally. The English countryside in April, which the poet Robert Browning paid homage to almost two centuries ago, probably never looked so tempting as it did to millions during lockdown.

An editorial in the *Lancet Planetary Health* journal has described this as a tale of two emergencies – Covid-19 and climate change – and commented on the differences in approach that have been taken. It points out that the way in which governments have responded to the pandemic would have been thought *'politically infeasible'* if applied to climate policy. We have had to change our whole lifestyle. This entire experience allows us to think much more creatively about what might be possible in tackling climate change.

The nations of the world signed up to the Sustainable Development Goals (SDGs) in 2015. These consist of 17 ambitious goals covering everything from health and gender to energy and climate, and all are to be achieved by 2030. They are *'a blueprint to achieve a better and more sustainable future for all'*.

This chapter follows the SDGs in how it discusses sustainability. It is about sustainability in the round; and about addressing economic, social and political issues, as much as environmental matters.

The chapter builds on many of the topics that have already been mentioned. The potential of communities, for example, and the power of nature to heal and create health. And in discussing planetary health, it adds another dimension to the idea that the health of individuals is linked to the health of communities by linking the health of our communities to the health of the planet.

And it reminds us all that today's young people will be the inheritors both of our debts and of the decisions that have been constantly put off, delayed and deferred.

The chapter starts in a vertical farm established four years ago in South East London, and where I have recently become a non-executive director.

***

Jamie Burrows had become very interested in urbanisation and public health while working as a management consultant. And, like increasing numbers of his generation, he wanted to do his own thing, control his own destiny and be creative. Food production, he decided, was a good option. Everyone needs food and it has an enormous impact on health.

He settled on the idea of creating a vertical farm using the latest technology and locating it in an urban area. He could see there were many benefits in doing so. Growing food locally would create jobs, he could save 'food miles' by distributing the produce on public transport, and he could control the nutritional quality and content.

With the support of his wife and co-founder, Marie, he formed Vertical Future in 2016 and I visited his first farm soon afterwards, in a regeneration area in Deptford. The farm, which is housed in an old factory building, has been converted into workshop units and is creating jobs in an area of high unemployment.

Deptford Dockyard had been a very important naval base, building and supplying ships for centuries since its foundation by King Henry VIII in 1513. It had been known as the *'cradle of the navy'* and was the site where Queen Elizabeth I had knighted Sir Francis Drake after his circumnavigation of the globe. But those days are long gone and, after years of decline, Deptford is now a fast-developing area with a diverse population, and a range of markets and small independent shops and venues.

It was a strange otherworldly experience walking upstairs in an old and rather neglected building with no carpets or wallpaper, no glossy entrance or smart reception, through a door into a pristine and clean high-tech environment bathed in purple light. Inside the growing room were stacks of metal trays five high, each containing rows and rows of small plants lit from above by the strange light and with their own water supply. This relatively small space could produce about five tonnes of produce every week.

The unit currently grows 85 different varieties of plant; about 30 of them are baby leaf plants for salads, while others are mints, herbs and more substantial bean shoots. They are grown quickly in highly controlled conditions that guarantee their nutritional qualities and without the use of any pesticides, herbicides or fungicides. This makes their produce better than organic or, in the words of Jamie and Marie, *'post-organic'*. Crops are harvested during the night and delivered to hundreds of restaurants, shops and homes in the early morning. They can be grown to order if a chef or aspiring home cook wants something in particular for their menu or creation.

Jamie is very interested in health and health education and, even while growing his business, has found time for local school children to visit, made links with local colleges, and has developed ideas about a more extensive community role. This is a highly technical business, which relies on expertise from plant technologists, engineers and IT specialists. But it can also provide training for local people, creating opportunities that weren't there before.

Vertical farming is a very simple concept, although technically very sophisticated, and it is clearly scalable across the country. I talked to Jamie about the future. He told me there is a developing industry around the world. Some of it is on a very large scale with massive automated farms being created in industrial buildings on the edges of towns. Larger plants can be grown than Jamie and his 20 person team cultivate in Deptford: whole head lettuce, tomatoes, strawberries, for example. But anything with big roots, such as potatoes, are out. Vertical farms can also be used to grow other crops used in research and pharmaceuticals, and in other botanical products.

Jamie plans to stay true to his original ideas about localness, maximum health benefits and guaranteed quality. He has also had discussions with partners about how he can reduce the impact of the electricity the farm uses. There are options for the future.

Like everyone else at the moment, of course, he is re-evaluating his plans. The virus, if anything, is likely to accelerate demand for locally sourced food.

***

I have been struck throughout my journey by the number of people I have met who are combining more than one purpose or goal in their organisations and activities. Jamie runs a for profit business but is also aiming to achieve social goals, not as a charitable act but as part of the core role of the business and central to the brand.

Paula Gamester of the Sewing Rooms, whose work is described in Chapter 7, runs a social enterprise, using business practices to achieve social goals. She told me about the importance of bringing money into Skelmersdale, improving the local economy, alongside her work with isolated people, newly arrived refugees and others. Pam Warhurst, of Incredible Edible, a community interest company described in Chapter 8, has established community gardens, supports community shops, runs training programmes, and is seeking to change NHS and government practice.

None of these enterprises fits easily into traditional categories or silos, or lines up with the responsibilities of government or local authority departments. This is part of the problem, of course, and why government finds it so difficult to work with many of these organisations. Everyone wants cross-silo, cross-sector, cross-government working in theory, but it's very hard to do in practice.

National membership body Social Enterprise UK describes social enterprises as a *'hidden revolution'*. It estimated in 2018 that there were more than 100,000 social enterprises in the UK employing around 2 million people and contributing £60 billion to the economy annually. These figures are larger than the Government's estimates because there is no official census and definitions differ. The Government, for example, excludes the 17,000 employed by the Nationwide, a mutual building society.

Social enterprises can have many different legal structures but, according to Social Enterprise UK, they are defined by five key points. They have a clear social or environmental mission set out in their governing documents; receive at least half their income from trading; are controlled or owned in the interests of their social mission; reinvest or give away at least half their profits or surpluses towards their social purpose; and are transparent about how they operate and their impact.

The Big Issue must be one of the best known social enterprises in the country. Founded by Lord John Bird in 1991 as a way of offering homeless people the chance to earn a living, it offers *'a hand up, not a hand out'*. And in the process, it supports improvements in their health and wellbeing.

Half the £2.50 cover price of the magazine goes to the vendor. Over the years, more than 90,000 people have been vendors and earned between them £115 million. Now, because of the virus, they are off the streets and, in many cases, have been taken to hotels being used as temporary accommodation. John and the team have responded by producing *The Big Issue* as a subscription service to maintain some income for the vendors while they are in isolation. But he also argues that in future we should *'accommodate the homeless within our society and not outside it, so they're not just an appendage to our lives'*.

Doing something dramatic about accommodating homeless people in this way is just another of those *'politically infeasible'* things referred to in the *Lancet* editorial. We can do this in these strange times. Why can't we do something similar in more normal times?

The Big Issue organisation has grown over the years and now performs three other roles in addition to publishing the magazine. In 2005, it set up Big Issue Invest, the first *'social merchant bank'*, which invests in social enterprises to drive social change and improvement. It advises on £150 million of investment and has already supported more than 300 enterprises with sums ranging from £20,000 to £3 million, and it has affected the lives of an estimated 1 million people.

The Big Issue Foundation is an independent charity set up in 1995 to support vendors in securing a better future for themselves. It seeks to tackle the fundamental issues attached to social and financial exclusion by working with individuals who have made the first step towards working themselves out of poverty through selling the magazine. It has worked successfully with 40,000 people over the years. In the words of the charity, it *'focuses on boosting self-esteem and helping vendors to reclaim their citizenship in order to deliver brighter futures'*.

The latest venture is The Big Issue Shop, which will sell products from social enterprises and *The Big Issue* itself. Every product will have a *'social echo'* to it by contributing to social good somewhere in the world. It is only the latest step in a journey that John Bird describes as *'dismantling poverty through creating opportunity'*. Dismantling poverty is one of the most important things that can be done to improve health.

John and other pioneers are following in a great tradition dating back to the 19th century and earlier, when charismatic individuals set out to tackle the social problems of the day. Social enterprises have strong links with another great tradition of co-operatives and mutual organisations, which grew up alongside methodism and socialism in the working class towns of the North of England. It is perhaps no surprise that the Sewing Rooms is based in Skelmersdale and Incredible Edible, with its community action and support for community shops, started in Todmorden, only seven miles from where the Rochdale Society of Equitable Pioneers set up its first Co-operative Society store in 1844.

Local authorities, NHS trusts, universities, football clubs and longstanding local businesses identified with a particular location have all been described recently as *'anchor organisations'*, whose activities not only bring wealth into an area – by employing people, for example – but can also strengthen it by how they behave and spend their resources. Many of them are now explicitly recognising their role as anchors and setting out to purchase and recruit locally, and to support their community and its activities in whatever way they can.

It is part of the core role of local authorities, of course, to promote the economic and social development of their areas. The Borough of Newham in East London exemplifies one modern version of this with its *Community Wealth Building Strategy*, launched in January 2020, which seeks to boost the income of the area and keep wealth in the local economy. Like others, the council is seeking to source goods and services locally and ethically, and be a living-wage employer. Preston City Council in Lancashire and others are similarly engaged in building the local economy in this way.

Anchor organisations can also play a leading role in creating a circular economy, in which waste is reduced to a minimum and products are reused, repaired, repurposed and recycled within an economy. This can create further value as well as reduce waste. It contrasts with the *linear* economy, which operates on a take-make-consume-dispose pattern.

***

Public institutions and social enterprises all have social goals because of their very nature, but some big businesses are now also adopting social responsibilities. In 2019, I attended a meeting of philanthropists and business leaders in Geneva that was looking at future trends globally. There was very little discussion of pandemics but I was struck by how much of the discussion was about localness – *place*, in other words – and responsibilities to stakeholders.

I talked with an Italian chair of a company that had been set up two generations earlier by his family. He was the biggest employer in his city, and he had an inherited sense of the company's position in the community and its responsibilities towards the city, its environment and inhabitants. It had become a Certified B Corporation, a designation that describes an organisation that is *'a new kind of business that balances purpose and profit'.* The B Corps are legally required to consider the impact of their decisions on their workers, customers, suppliers, community and the environment. They are *'driving a global movement of people using business as a force for good'.*

It will be interesting to see how these B Corps have dealt with these responsibilities during the pandemic and whether they have been able to live up to these high ambitions. And whether they have responded differently from other businesses.

This approach fits very naturally with the family owned business of the Italian chair whom I talked to, but big companies with family and local roots have become much rarer in the UK in recent years. There are now few such anchor business organisations. Many have been taken over and merged into national and international corporations, with global supply chains and without any local loyalties.

There was much talk of responsible businesses at the annual meeting of the World Economic Forum, held in Davos in January 2020, and attended by global finance, business and political leaders. This reflected wider discussions within business circles and centred around saving the planet, fairer economics and better business. They appear to have been driven mainly by concerns about the impacts of climate change but there were also concerns raised about record levels of inequality and the public image of finance and business.

The truth behind these positive words will be reflected in how these groups deal with the impact of the pandemic. More mundanely, one may ask whether any of them can resist the lure of a takeover that promises a 50 per cent return and involves massive closures, job losses and wholesale asset stripping. There will be plenty of such opportunities as Covid-19 takes its toll.

It was Lord Michael Heseltine, the former Conservative deputy prime minister, who recently wrote in his blueprint for the future of English towns and cities that *'capitalism knows no morality'*. And Adam Smith, the great 18th century proponent of commerce as the organising principle for society, argued that there is a need for *'maintaining those public institutions and public works, which may be in the highest degree advantageous to a great society ...'* but can't be funded by individuals.

The pandemic has demonstrated the need for active government intervention in times of crisis, as will be discussed in Chapter 15. It is worth noting here that the Bank of England recognised the climate crisis in regulation for the first time in late 2019. The major UK banks and insurers will be obliged to report on the potential financial damage to their businesses from climate change for the first time in 2021. As the Bank's then governor, Mark Carney, pointed out, climate change will affect the value of virtually every financial asset. And this public reporting will surely bring about some welcome longer term thinking and lead to changes in policy and action.

Climate change and the regulatory and political response to environmental problems are increasingly seen as two of the biggest long term threats to the financial industry. And, in turn, they will threaten industry more generally, as well as jobs, security and health and wellbeing.

***

All of this fits within the bigger picture of planetary health. The Rockefeller Foundation–Lancet Commission on Planetary Health brought the term into common use with the publication of its 2015 report. It is worth quoting its definition of planetary health in full: *'the achievement of the highest attainable standard of health, wellbeing and equity worldwide through judicious attention to the human systems – political, economic and social – that shape the future of humanity and the Earth's natural systems that define the safe environmental limits within which humanity can flourish.*

'Put simply, planetary health is the health of human civilisation and the state of the natural systems on which it depends.'

Planetary health is a powerful idea that links together many of the issues raised in *Health is made at home* – we depend on our community's health and it depends on the planet's health. Action at every level: the personal, community and global are all necessary.

We are already seeing the impact of climate change globally from fires in Australia, drought in East Africa, migration in Europe, and exceptional weather and flooding in many parts of the world. But the response to it has been inadequate and piecemeal at best, and bedevilled by politics and vested interests. Climate change is now widely seen to be an emergency, although some countries and groups still deny it. And greenhouse gas emissions are still not under control.

The contrast with the Covid-19 pandemic is glaring. We were badly unprepared for the pandemic despite the science and the warnings that have been available for years. Policy may have been made on the hoof but the speed of response has ultimately been remarkable. The immediacy of the threat is one reason for the difference. None of us, politicians included, could ignore people dying and hospitals being swamped.

Climate change requires action by us all as individuals, communities, organisations and countries. Some of this is difficult, of course; but technology, nudging and government intervention could make an enormous impact. The biggest difference from Covid-19, however, is the existence of so many and such powerful vested interests in the status quo, from the energy producers to the airlines, the car manufacturers and the farmers. As the *Lancet* has pointed out, there are no obvious beneficiaries from a worsening of the pandemic.

Tackling climate change will have profound effects on these industries, with farming, for example, transformed by innovations like vertical farms as well as by less meat production, a reduction in chemical use, more local produce, and less 'slash and burn' and forest clearance globally.

Covid-19 has led to a national protectionism and *'every country for itself'* attitude in the clamour for protective equipment, ventilators and health workers. The US has abdicated its leadership role and while the World Health Organization has co-ordinated some of the scientific response, it has been powerless to enforce any action. An immediate test, as I write this in May 2020, is how well will the rich countries of the North support the poorer countries of the South in tackling the pandemic and its aftermath? Will we accelerate recruitment of health workers from these countries, and thereby damage their health systems? And will we leave the support role to China?

None of this augurs well for concerted global action in the future. This is a topic we will return to in Chapter 16.

***

The big idea that we can learn from the health creators in this chapter is to copy Jamie Burrows and Lord John Bird and *be entrepreneurial, experiment and learn by doing.*

Neither of them were following a blueprint. Lord Andrew Mawson, whose work is described in Chapter 8, didn't set out 30 years ago to build a joined-up neighbourhood or expect to be involved in creating healthy towns and cities. He and his colleagues simply saw what needed doing in front of them and got on with it. They learned by experimentation, with one thing leading to another. There are further examples later in this book. Richard Howells didn't have the whole plan for Tribe in his head, as will be described in Chapter 11. And the Nursing Now campaign, which will be described in Chapter 12, was launched with a vision and set of aims but has also taken opportunities, many of which were not anticipated, as they arose.

The simple underlying point here is that we need to discover what works in today's changing environment. This is new territory for us all and the only way forward is experimentation and learning by doing. Be entrepreneurial.

There are two recommendations for government in this chapter. The first is to *support the Wellbeing of Future Generations Bill*. This Bill, introduced in January 2020 in the House of Lords by Lord Bird, will require public bodies to act to improve the environmental, economic, social and cultural wellbeing of current and future generations.

Government needs to be much better at long term thinking. There are many examples in *Health is made at home* where action today could head off longer term problems: from a better approach to excluding children from school, to ensuring pensioners live in healthy homes. Short term approaches can damage people's health and lives, and they tend to be more expensive in the long run.

Short term decision making has particularly acute implications for younger people. Too often, policy decisions are made without consideration of the long term implications that they might have on future generations.

The Future Generations Bill is based on the Welsh Government's Well-being of Future Generations (Wales) Act 2015, which has the main aim of guaranteeing that public bodies and ministers act in accordance with the future generations principle; the Bill seeks to extend the Act's remit to the whole of the UK.

The principles in the Bill include balancing long term and short term needs, acting in a preventive way, and seeking to forecast emerging risks. It calls for a future generation commissioner and a Joint Parliamentary Committee on Future Generations, whose role will entail scrutinising legislation and holding the Government to account on its short term policy decisions.

The second recommendation for government is *to embed the importance of planetary health within all government policies*. This will provide a clear focus for cross-departmental action on climate change.

CHAPTER ELEVEN

TAKING CONTROL OF OUR HEALTH

In the beginning, Richard Howells was simply trying to find the best way to provide care for his mother. But he ended up improving care for people across her home county of Shropshire. At the time of writing, he is supporting authorities and communities with their response to Covid-19 and, over time, may well play a fundamental role in improving care across the whole country.

He is using his technical and business skills, and the capability of his company, Bronze Labs, to strengthen local communities and give more control to patients and their carers.

Richard is a successful digital entrepreneur. A mathematician and software engineer, he had worked for some of the biggest names in the industry but became fed up with the culture of these companies, and so set up Bronze Labs in 2011.

There's a management saying that *'culture always trumps strategy'*, meaning that your stated intention and plans can all too often be derailed by old working habits and the internal workings and bureaucracy of an organisation. It's one of the reasons why organisations find it so difficult to change direction and reinvent themselves, and why mergers often fail to achieve their full potential. Culture gets in the way.

Richard's approach was to make culture his strategy in Bronze Labs. He developed a culture of problem solving and teamwork: focused and with attention to detail while being experimental and innovative.

It worked brilliantly. He and his team were extremely successful; winning contracts from Formula 1 and the RAF for head-up displays and predictive data systems, they have gone on to obtain further industry recognition while securing more major contracts. His style and approach were key to what happened when his mother was diagnosed with a progressive illness, which meant that she would need increasing levels of care for the rest of her life. She lives in rural Shropshire in a 'care black hole', which is poorly served by the NHS and other agencies. Richard could simply have paid privately for her care. Instead, he set out to understand the problems and see if he could use his skills and experience to fix them.

He had spent 11 hours in A&E in Telford with his mother and, seeing how pressurised the clinical staff were, he recognised that a good part of the problem was that there was so little care available in the community. His problem-solving instincts came to the fore and he wanted to do something about it.

Bronze Labs' core activity is all about transforming the way organisations manage assets and data, and developing Internet of Things (IoT) technologies that can be used in any kind of industry or setting. And Richard recognised that they could apply very directly to the problems he was seeing in front of him.

The initial reaction of the authorities was negative. The NHS locally was apathetic but he persevered and, using his credibility as a businessman, he managed to arrange meetings with the Department of Health and various agencies. He told me he had 26 meetings but no practical result. There was plenty of enthusiasm for his developing ideas but nothing happened.

He decided to use his own money and the skills of his Bronze Labs team. He started working with the Oswestry Community Action charity to see how it could use his technologies to support some of the very small organisations that provided care locally. He was asked by the local council to look at how it could make payments to support these organisations. Richard responded by dealing with that issue and going much further by developing software that used all the available data from all the agencies to map out and predict need in the different communities. It was a revelation for the council staff.

By now Richard had become fully engaged in solving the problems he was encountering and he decided to set up a new organisation, the Tribe Project, which has the wider goal of promoting community cohesion and community care. In his words, its mission is *'to increase social action, improving the quality of life for millions of vulnerable people'*.

He is spending £3.6 million of his own money on Tribe and, even more remarkably, he has switched the whole resource of his company to developing the software and artificial intelligence tools to support it – even turning down a contract that Bronze Labs had won to work on the Royal Navy's Type 25 frigate.

Of course, Richard's accountants said he was crazy. But his colleagues stayed with him, with only one leaving for more conventional commercial work elsewhere. You can hear Richard's passion for what he is doing as he talks about Tribe. This isn't about money. And, he said, all his colleagues have had experience of someone close to them needing care and they share his passion.

He is quoted on the Tribe website as saying that this is about *'people having a purpose'* and *'we have stopped believing in people. We have become cynical.'*

By this stage he had met Siân Lockwood of Community Catalysts who helped him understand the skills needed for people to become carers and volunteers, and introduced him to Skills for Care, the organisation responsible for standards and training in this area. It was another important piece of the jigsaw and he worked with Skills for Care on how best to train people as carers. Here, once again, Richard introduced new ideas including the use of virtual reality headsets for some of the initial training.

Tribe now classifies carers on its system into three levels. In broad terms, these are: undertaking minor tasks such as cooking; offering some personal care; and providing full care for people who are very frail or disabled, physically and/or mentally. Skills for Care specified the training needed.

The more that Richard looked into the provision of care, the more he saw things that could be improved. He calculated that about 900 carers are leaving their jobs every day in the UK, mainly due to poor pay and conditions. And there was a mismatch, he told me, between the values of the carers with their high degree of empathy and what they could achieve in reality. They were too often expected to carry out tasks in 15 to 30 minute visits and then move on to the next person. It was deeply frustrating.

'You may get tea and toast but nothing else,' Richard said. *'It really makes no difference.'*

'And,' he told me, *'the people being looked after are mostly lovely people who feel for the carers and tell them 'Go on, I'll be ok'.'*

Richard realised that the carers, who were mostly on zero hours contacts and often with several companies, could operate as individual micro-businesses if they had support to find clients, be paid and receive regularly updated training. His solution was to create an Uber-style app, which allows anyone to search on their phone or computer for carers locally who have the level of skill they need. Equally, it enables carers to find clients.

He backed this up with a system that uses blockchain technology to transfer funds to the carer's account. There are quality controls, too, and only carers trained to one of the three levels can use the system.

These arrangements cut out the need for a care agency and therefore allow carers to keep more of the fee paid by the client – or reduce the fees – and offer a better service. It also reduces a council's administration and commissioning costs, where they are responsible for paying for the care.

The app can also be used for voluntary work, for connecting people, and for creating and supporting community activities of all kinds. The main elements of Tribe had now been brought together.

As Richard said: *'We are tackling challenges created by an ageing population and dated care models, while creating new opportunities for all. Tribe rethinks micro-commissioning, social prescribing and social action to improve quality of life for older people and generate thousands of new paid and voluntary opportunities.'*

And also, very importantly, *'the technology reduces pressure on public services to address the challenges of an ageing population, loneliness and inequality across the UK'.*

Tribe could hardly be more timely or important. The need for care is growing and the supply of carers is shrinking just at a time when Brexit and new immigration rules make it more difficult to recruit people from other countries. Other nationalities currently make up about one in six of all paid carers. There is a developing care crisis, which Covid-19 has helped make visible to the public and the media.

This whole approach can also reduce costs, or at least stop them rising, and provide employment in the sort of jobs that won't be taken over by machines. Moreover, because GDP is calculated on the values of transactions, the creation of many micro-enterprises will have the effect of increasing GDP.

Tribe looks like a win all round and councils as far apart as Essex, Dorset and Birmingham, as well as Shropshire, have started to work with Richard on implementing it in part or in full. This is giving him and the councils the opportunity to trial aspects and work out how best to achieve the full potential of the system.

Richard's aim is to be able to offer these systems to the NHS and local authorities across the whole country, and he is willing to provide the intellectual property and technology on a break-even basis as a social benefit and example of 'tech for good'. Moreover, surpluses will be reinvested in the organisation with a part distributed as a dividend to the carers involved.

But despite winning more awards for his work on Tribe and receiving praise from government ministers, Richard is finding it extraordinarily difficult to move forward at the scale and pace he needs to make a really significant impact on the problems faced by the NHS and social care. There is a lot of interest and much enthusiasm but not yet the strategic drive necessary to release the benefits of the system.

The Covid-19 pandemic has, of course, brought all this into sharp focus. We can now all see just how important the care sector is, and how poor are the conditions and pay of so many carers. It is no surprise that increasing numbers of councils and clinical commissioning groups are looking to Richard for help as they grapple with the virus and its aftermath.

This brief account of Tribe only touches on some of the many twists and turns of a story which, I am sure, will be told in greater detail someday. And by then it will surely be a story with a more satisfactory ending than it has today.

Meanwhile Richard, as you might predict, is looking at the next steps and considering how his tools and techniques can be applied abroad on a for profit basis – with the ambition of creating the UK's first billion pound AI company.

Tribe exemplifies many of the themes of this book: the entrepreneurial learning by doing approach, the focus on community, the passion, the need for people to have relationships and meaning in their lives, and the need we all have for more control over our lives.

It is also reminiscent of pioneering examples I have seen elsewhere, such as Buurtzorg in the Netherlands where groups of self-organising nurses provide services for communities without a controlling head office or management centre.

Tribe is also an example of how someone from outside the system can bring new insight by applying their knowledge and skills. People like Richard Howells, or the hydraulics engineer I met in Sweden who suffered kidney failure and found himself needing to have dialysis three times a week to a hospital's timetable. It was debilitating and took over his whole life. He persuaded the clinical staff to teach him how to operate the machinery safely and to use the equipment at times that suited him. Now, any patients can opt to be trained and apply for swipe cards that give them access to the dialysis unit at any time of day and night to perform their own treatment. And the approach has spread to other hospitals and their patients. Giving them back control.

Tribe is, of course, on a much bigger scale with potentially a far greater impact across the whole health and care system.

***

I know from my own experience that one of the great frustrations of using the NHS or any health system is the feeling of being out of control, not knowing what is going on, and waiting around for others to make decisions or tell you what is happening.

Disease and accidents are disempowering enough, so are fear and anxiety, but many traditional systems and practices – and the hierarchy of power in healthcare – disable patients even more. Problems of anxiety and miscommunication are well documented with the result that not only do patients feel powerless but, part of the time, so do their clinicians.

This is partly about attitudes and behaviours, but it is also about putting as many tools as possible into the hands of patients so that they can understand what is happening, ask the right questions and make decisions.

There has been a strong emphasis on changing behaviours in recent years, moving away from what one might caricature as the top-down 'doctor knows best' approach, with its old language of patients complying with their treatment and following instructions, to a more equal 'co-production' approach. Most doctors and other clinicians have always worked *with* their patients, and listening is a vital skill for any good clinician. Nurses, in particular, are mostly very good at 'walking alongside their patients' and helping them understand what is going on – a point we will return to in the next chapter.

Clinicians do generally know best, about the science at least. They have the knowledge that we as patients don't have. But they don't necessarily understand our circumstances, lives and preferences, all of which will influence the success of treatment and whether we follow their advice or not. There is a new movement, originating in the US, to replace the question *'what's the matter with you?'* with *'what matters to you?'*

This changes the dynamic and introduces a whole new set of considerations into a consultation: what are the most important symptoms to control? Can you follow this regime? Which are the best options for treatment, what sort of risks are you willing to take? It also lengthens the consultation which, in today's pressurised environment, is a major difficulty – and at least some of the problems of poor communication and misunderstandings are simply due to pressurised professionals working at pace.

There are also techniques and tools that can help patients have more control. Health education and health literacy need to be more central to general education, as does some understanding of probability. Health information needs to be more readily accessible and quality controlled. And new tools can provide rapid feedback and monitoring for patients and clinicians alike.

Stephen Friend is an American medical doctor who is also a serial entrepreneur and biomedical researcher. He is developing the use of feedback and predictive technology as Professor of Connected Medicine at Oxford. I have known him for some years as someone whose focus and passion are explicitly directed towards giving patients more control.

He is running several research programmes using wearable sensors – bracelets, watches, rings, even clothing – that can measure all kinds of physiological data, provide a record of any changes, and seek to link them with the circumstances that produced them. They provide useful feedback in treating diseases and can be used to help people wearing them improve their health as, indeed, some well-known commercially available devices already do.

One of his interests is chronic stress, which is a major underlying contributor to many of the leading causes of death globally. Use of wearable devices will provide data that can enable a better understanding of stress and the way it contributes to disease. Analysis of the data using AI will also allow patients and their clinicians to track symptoms so that they can forecast the onset or worsening of chronic diseases like arthritis, dementia and multiple sclerosis, predict acute episodes and, where possible, take evasive action.

This measuring and monitoring will also be very useful at times of transition in people's lives, such as pregnancy and the menopause. Or in the stressful years of adolescence when some mental illnesses manifest themselves for the first time, and can potentially be treated or managed before they become chronic or uncontrollable.

Stephen has set up a not for profit organisation called 4YouandMe, which has the mission of partnering with *'scientists, clinicians, activists, policy makers and people to gain insights about health from digital tools. Our coalitions aim to develop methods using integrated novel measurements of individuals to produce reliable personalised predictions of paths towards wellness and away from disease.'*

Interestingly, in the context of this book, Stephen sees the organisation as being about communities that can support each other with their choices and decisions, so that individuals will not just rely on the technical support of their clinicians.

4YouandMe is about to start a study on menopause using wearables and which will be owned and led by the participating women. They will set the questions, identify what they want to learn, and support each other on their journeys. He suggests that, in due course, this could become a clinical group co-operative and take on a life of its own.

Stephen's work is about practical approaches that can change patients' experience of their disease but will also, potentially, have profound effects on how we understand disease and organise health services. There is, for example, the potential to change our definitions of bipolar disease, autism, depression, anxiety and other syndromes. These, as he explains, have been built up from what are essentially snapshots of behaviour observed by clinicians and supplemented by patients' own, often incomplete, descriptions. Measuring physiological signs will add to and quite probably change our knowledge of these conditions. Similarly, such measurements should help us to understand better the non-genetic components of disease.

Looking ahead, Stephen argues that health services will change with financial and other benefits for society if we follow through the logic of this patient-centred approach. Currently, he points out, we are stuck in an acute hospital and treatment based model, where all the incentives for organisations are to promote treatment and thereby increase income. There is a new model emerging from the work of pioneers in this field which, in his words, *'support and nourish the return of agency to individuals'*.

We are only in the foothills of these developments and can only imagine how these approaches will eventually help us fine-tune our habits and our bodies for maximum efficiency and minimal damage. Linked with greater understanding of disease and the ageing process, we can see how lives could potentially be significantly extended and health vastly improved as we age.

Returning to the here and now, Stephen also introduced me to patient groups who are leading the way in some of the research on their own diseases. There are organisations that promote advocacy by patients and others that offer support. There are also groups of people each with a specific disease, renal cancer for example, who share their experiences with each other. They can report on how they are reacting to new treatments and the perceived impact of a drug. And they can do so quicker than clinicians, whose reporting is more restricted by the needs of science and hard evidence.

These networks are contributing to the rapid spread of some treatments and suggesting new opportunities for more formal research. They also offer opportunities for sharing personal experiences, provide purpose and meaning, and give some control to patients.

This combination of advocacy, sharing experience and knowledge, and community support was, of course, how many people with HIV/AIDS in the 1980s and 90s led the way in tackling the disease – even without the advantages we now have of the internet, email, social media, AI and machine learning.

***

Taking control of our health is not all about technology. It is also about dealing with perceptions and prejudices that have, in some cases, become deeply institutionalised.

We discussed community in the sense of geographical community in earlier chapters and stressed the importance of building communities in this chapter with the Tribe Project. But there are other types of communities, too. They are about an identity that we give ourselves or others give us: from faith communities, the gay or LGBT+ communities, to black, Asian and minority ethnic communities – a term incidentally that ignores the many differences between such groups.

These different communities all have specific health needs, which may not be met by the generic services of the NHS. Women and men have different needs and experience health services differently, as do other genders. Different ethnic minorities have different risk factors with, for example, people of south Asian origin much more likely to have heart disease and be diabetic. Adolescents also have different needs from both children and adults.

Diagnosis and treatment have typically been based on the symptoms and needs of male patients so that women having a heart attack and displaying different symptoms, for example, may not be treated appropriately. This has led to avoidable deaths and poor treatment for many women. Covid-19, of course, has killed about twice as many men as women. And people from black, Asian and minority ethnic backgrounds appear to be four times as likely to die from the virus than people from the majority population for reasons that are not yet understood.

The NHS has become far better in recent years in identifying and understanding these differing needs. But there is a continuing requirement to disaggregate data by age, gender, ethnicity and other factors in order to understand what is happening, and thereby enable clinicians to treat patients more effectively and allow patients to take more control of their health. This is territory where AI will have enormous impact in the years to come, not only in identifying the needs of different groups but also in identifying the different variants of disease, immune responses and the impact of co-morbidities.

I have discussed these issues many times with Yvonne Coghill. She is a nurse from an African-Caribbean background. I mentored her for a period when I was chief executive of the NHS. In truth, it was co-mentoring as I learned so much from her and her very different perspective on the organisation, as well as life more generally. Yvonne is now head of race equality for the NHS and has built up an impressive knowledge of these issues.

There has been progress with some of the most obvious presenting issues, such as Sickle Cell Disease, which affects men and boys of African heritage, and in tackling diabetes in South Asian populations. But there is much more to do; for example, in improving care for young black men with mental health and addiction problems.

There is a very long-standing problem here. Young black men are about four times as likely as white young men to be admitted to a mental hospital and are more likely to be detained involuntarily. And, once admitted, they are more likely to be put into seclusion. There is also some evidence that black men are sometimes given different diagnoses from white people displaying the same symptoms.

This is a very complex area where a number of different issues can influence what happens. The commission I chaired on mental health admissions in 2014 argued for the introduction of a new patient care standard, which could be used to monitor these differences in individual trusts and seek explanations and provoke action.

There is also a very practical underlying point. As Jacqui Dyer, an expert by experience and mental health equalities adviser to NHS England, explains: *'Psychiatry and psychology normally rely on theories based on Eurocentric ideas and philosophies.'*

'How can you get to recovery,' she asks, *'when you are not dealing with our issues?'* There is beginning to be a shift in thinking with new research underway based on different cultural premises and ideas, while several projects have been started to design and introduce new ideas and approaches.

These issues are most apparent with young black men of African-Caribbean heritage but also apply to other people of different cultural backgrounds. I discussed this point with Poppy Jaman, who described her own periods of mental illness in Chapter 3. She has a Bangladeshi background and recognises from her own experience that the people who were attempting to treat her simply didn't understand the issues with which she was grappling.

But, as Yvonne Coghill says, this is not just about diseases but about far wider organisational and societal issues. She has been responsible for introducing and monitoring a Workforce Race Equality Standard, which is used to measure, trust by trust, whether white and black staff are treated the same way on opportunities and disciplinary issues. Its findings act as a spur for organisations to improve. There are still big differences across organisations and the NHS as a whole is still 'snow-capped', becoming whiter the higher up the organisation you go.

Yvonne has pointed to strong evidence that morale among staff is associated with quality of care. Morale matters, and if black staff are feeling undervalued, it will rub off on their patients and make it more difficult for black patients to feel in control of what is happening to them within the system.

She has also introduced me to the phenomenon known as 'weathering'. Being different from the majority population in any area brings with it increased stress which, we now know, increases levels of cortisol in the body and thereby weakens the immune system. This in turn is associated with many leading causes of death, as noted earlier in discussing Stephen Friend's work.

'Being black in a white society,' Yvonne says, *'is bad for your health.'* While the research on weathering has focused on black people who are visibly different to the majority population where they live, its findings may well apply equally to minorities of all kinds. Constant additional stress, even at low levels, is bad for your health. Ultimately, this effect will only disappear when there is true equity across our society but, in the meantime, there are ways of mitigating the effect. Some of it is through the sorts of actions taken by Yvonne and Jacqui from within the system, and some is through external advocacy and action from black groups.

My wife Siân and I met Heather Nelson, chief executive of the Black Health Initiative, in a community cafe in a community hub near the centre of Leeds. The centre houses a primary care practice and a library, and provides a range of services for local people. The cafe itself is staffed by unemployed people, several of whom have gone on to get jobs thanks to the experience they gained. Bright and airy, the cafe was obviously a public building but it had a friendly atmosphere and was clearly well used by local groups as well as individuals.

The Black Health Initiative was set up with two related purposes: to provide services for black people, and to lobby the NHS and other authorities to improve their services for black people. It runs programmes on health and wellbeing for both men and women, and a Fusion Cafe once a week where local people can meet and talk over a healthy meal. It is used mainly by older people from the Caribbean but some young people come too, for a meal, social contact, exercise and for information about services and organisations in the city. And, Heather told us, some 'non-visible minorities' also use it, mainly older Irish and Scottish people who live locally.

Heather's advocacy is based firmly in experience on the ground, linked with the latest epidemiological and clinical research. The Black Health Initiative has pressed the case for changes in cancer policy and mental health to serve better the needs of people from black communities. In cancer, she told me, black people are far more likely to present late with advanced symptoms and there is a need for more health education aimed at different groups.

Heather's expertise and her evident persistence mean that the Black Health Initiative is now recognised by the NHS centrally, and her and her team are regularly consulted on policies. It is difficult though, she said, because people don't stay long in post and she finds herself regularly having to educate a new group of policy makers and officials.

I asked about funding. It is hand to mouth: a bit of lottery money and some services are commissioned by the NHS locally, but it's always project and programme money, which doesn't cover core costs and leaves them constantly searching for funds. And, she told me wryly, she keeps getting GPs making social prescribing referrals – wanting to prescribe social activities, such as dancing, for their patients instead of drugs – but there's no money to run them.

Siân and I left the cafe wondering if this wasn't all the wrong way around and upside down. If the NHS valued the programme's input, shouldn't it be paying for it? And wouldn't it be better to invest in community buildings and activities so that people wouldn't need to visit their GPs in the first place?

***

There is another dimension, too, of faith and spirituality. Churches, temples, synagogues and mosques can play an enormous role in creating health – and many do. There are literally thousands of faith groups offering support, giving guidance and providing funding for health activities for their congregations and the wider public. And many of the people mentioned in this book are motivated by their faith.

I spoke to Pastor Paul James, who works in Ealing, about health and faith. His church, Harrow International Christian Centre, has worshippers from 40 countries who come together in one congregation. Many of them, he told me, are local health professionals from the NHS. The church also has an outreach programme where once a month doctors and nurses are available to provide information and advice.

His church plays its part in the local community although its whole purpose is religious. Pastor Paul talked to me about ministering to the whole person. *'Think of yourself as God does,'* he said, *'positively.'* He went on to talk about how uncertain some people are about who they are. And he said the church should be the solution to so much loneliness and the care of the elderly, and much more. But this was all about God, he said, and the whole person.

There was an echo here of the holistic approach adopted by so many people in this book, I said: *'Health is so much more than the absence of disease.'*

'Yes,' he replied, *'but salvation is not just a coping strategy.'*

This takes health right out of the realm of public service, charity, politics and rights, and places it firmly within the wider spiritual world.

For many people this is of fundamental importance.

***

There are so many different ways of taking back control of our health. Only a few are sketched out here but they give a sense of what can be done – and what is being done all over the country.

The big idea in this chapter is about *control.* The autonomy, the ability to act, and not being at the mercy of others. This in itself is good for you.

In sickness and in health.

CHAPTER TWELVE

GLOBAL ACTION

The earlier chapters have been about people from outside the health sector creating health and the conditions for us to be healthy – and beginning to influence the whole health and care system. This one is rather different. It is about health professionals and others linking with partners globally and bringing back new ideas to the UK. These groups are also health creators and changing the way we think and talk about health.

We now all know a lot more than we ever wanted to about the disadvantages of living in such an interconnected world, owing to the Covid-19 pandemic.

There are, however, some advantages too. These interconnections bring with them incredible opportunities for joint action, learning and development. Many of the organisations mentioned in this book, such as forest schools and Incredible Edible, have foreign links; others, like the City Mental Health Alliance, have ambitions to expand overseas. And there are many UK organisations that link with overseas groups for mutual benefit and learning, and to work together on global issues.

This sharing is very powerful. It is now more important than ever that we work together globally despite – and also because of – the grim state of international politics and the many conflicts around the world.

I have spent the last 14 years working on global health, mainly in Africa, and have been personally involved in some of what I write about in this chapter. One of the themes I have pursued is the idea that we, in the industrialised countries of the West, can learn a great deal about health from people in these countries.

There is also a great deal that they can learn from us. In the words of the Institute for Healthcare Improvement: *'Everyone has something to teach and everyone has something to learn.'*

I believe we need to take this further into what I call *'co-development'*; where people from different countries and cultures work together on our shared issues. The whole language of international development with its top-down connotation of people from *developed* countries helping the *underdeveloped* is no longer appropriate. It must be two way.

***

Covid-19 has already wreaked havoc among relatively wealthy countries in the North.

Its impact in southern countries is still uncertain at the time of writing. Some African countries with their experience of Ebola and other epidemics appear to be coping very well, while elsewhere, Brazil for example, there is acute suffering. The biggest impact may well come from a downturn in economic trade and a reduction in development funding.

THET, the Tropical Health and Education Trust, supports many partnerships between NHS organisations and their peers in low and middle income countries, and manages a government grant scheme. It has responded to the crisis by setting up a programme to use these partnerships to support these countries in tackling the virus. Many are already doing so.

The programme is designed to identify priorities for support in each country, provide training and advice, and offer psychological support and solidarity by maintaining links. THET has also set up a rapid response fund for partnerships to support frontline health workers and health managers, and a mechanism for sharing learning between partnerships and countries.

This is a natural extension of THET's role which, in addition to supporting partnerships, involves running large health system and health workforce capacity development programmes in Ethiopia, Myanmar, Somalia, Tanzania, Uganda and Zambia. Their focus throughout is on supporting and developing health workers. THET was founded 25 years ago by Sir Eldryd Parry, a distinguished British physician, and ever since it has been training health workers to build a world where everyone has access to affordable and quality healthcare.

In the last ten years, THET has reached more than 100,000 health workers across 31 countries in Africa and Asia, in partnership with more than 130 UK institutions. It has also benefitted the UK, helping develop and revitalise thousands of NHS workers and bringing new ideas back to the UK.

Ben Simms, THET's chief executive, describes its role as *'working in partnership to support health workers across the world'*, and under his leadership, THET has developed a very professional and systematic approach to partnerships. THET's eight principles of partnership encapsulate the whole approach, covering areas such as being strategic, effective and sustainable, respectful and reciprocal, and committed to joint learning.

These principles reinforce many of the big ideas in this book: the importance of relationships, of communities, of connecting and communicating, and of being entrepreneurial and learning by doing.

And, of course, the importance of taking off our NHS spectacles and seeing the world differently.

Almost 40 years ago, another far-sighted clinician, Dr Nick Maurice, a GP in the town of Marlborough, set up the Marlborough Brandt Group. He was inspired by the Brandt Report, which described the enormous inequality between the North and the South, and he wanted to help build greater understanding between these two parts of the world and promote development.

The group set up a link in 1981 between Marlborough and Gunjur, a largely Muslim town in the Gambia, and organised visits both ways *'in the hope that by gaining a deeper understanding of each other through shared experiences and mutual exchange, this would educate not only those directly involved but politicians and the wider communities around them'*.

Over the years, about 2000 people have participated in visits between the two communities, staying with local people, working on local projects in both communities, and sharing ideas about education and development. The Group's current chair, Alex Davies, told me that it now concentrated on fundraising for projects and organisations in Gunjur, although there are still several visits from the UK each year.

Nick, meanwhile, has set up a new organisation called Thriving Through Venture, with Caro Strover, an educational psychologist. This involves young people with early signs of mental illness, such as lack of self-confidence, self-esteem and a sense of purpose, working with young Gambians on various projects.

The concepts of mutual understanding, equal partnerships and respectful behaviour, which underpin both THET's and the Marlborough Brandt Group's approaches, as well as the passion for change, are essential when working with people from other countries and cultures. Like others, I have seen too many examples of well-intentioned westerners arriving in southern communities with preconceived ideas about how they can sort out their problems. And then, of course, failing. We all need to support local people in doing what they know needs to be done – and this applies whether we are working in a housing estate in Cornwall or Bolton in the UK or in a community abroad.

And this sort of people to people relationship, rather than just government to government action, has a vital role to play in development and international relations more widely. We can all take a personal lead in this vital area.

***

There are other international health projects that are much more focused on the sharing of practical knowledge and skills. But they also have their mutual benefits, with each party gaining something. One of these was the challenge we set UK anaesthetists in Zambia. And they rose to it magnificently.

Dr Simon Miti, then the Permanent Secretary of the Zambian Department of Health, and I decided in 2008 to set up an anaesthetic training programme in the country. The idea was simple. Zambia didn't have any training programmes for pathologists, psychiatrists and anaesthetists and, as a result, had very few of these specialists. I was confident there would be British doctors who would be willing to help voluntarily. We decided to try to bring the two parts together.

In the longer term, we reasoned, the specialists we trained could become the trainers and the whole thing could become self-sustaining.

Inevitably, and particularly in the early days, it took time and considerable effort from Dr David Percy, a former GP and primary care postgraduate dean from the South of England. He was the key person who identified the doctors and made the practical arrangements, while I negotiated support from the Department for International Development (DFID) and agreed with THET that it would provide management support and governance. David spent a lot of time in Zambia in those early years building relationships and supporting the programmes.

The anaesthetic programme has been a wonderful collective effort involving more than 100 UK doctors over the years. Professor John Kinnear brought together other senior colleagues as well as UK trainees to provide the training and support in Zambia. The initial programme lasted four years and involved 23 Zambian trainees. It was highly organised, with a UK consultant appointed to the faculty of the National University, in Lusaka, to lead the work. An average of ten UK consultants a year made short visits of two to three weeks each to provide subspecialty training, while more junior UK doctors provided continuing supervision and training. There were also several visits each year from junior UK trainees.

And just as we had originally hoped, some of the newly trained anaesthetists became the trainers themselves, and others moved on to serve as heads of department in other hospitals around the country. It was a great success.

Neither the Zambians nor the Brits wanted the programme to stop when the DFID money ran out, so John and colleagues set up a charity to raise funds for its continuation and expansion. The Zambians could see that there was still more training to do and they wanted subspecialties to be developed. They also valued the personal and professional partnerships that were created.

It had been very successful for the UK too. The whole programme was very popular and beneficial for the training and experience of the UK trainees. And the senior consultants came back from their short stints in Zambia refreshed and with new motivation and ideas. It also led to lots of interesting research papers.

This short account underplays the enormous difficulties that John and colleagues had to overcome. Personnel changed in Zambia. And the Zambian Government changed its policy, as governments do. Training became the responsibility of another ministry and new relationships had to be forged. There were funding problems and logistical challenges, as well as all the difficulties of working in a health system with poor resources.

I talked to John about the programme in March 2020. He had temporarily given up his academic role and was working full time in intensive care in Southend fighting the virus. I asked what had motivated him. Interest, he said, it was a challenge and a problem he thought he could solve, and he had a deep affinity for Africa having trained there. *'At the beginning,'* he said, *'we were starting from zero and it sounded impossible. But I did the original needs assessment and realised that enough people wanted it and that there was a way through.'*

As with other pioneers and health creators in *Health is made at home,* this is a story of taking control, determination, being entrepreneurial and building good relationships.

The Zambia partnership is still going strong more than a decade after it started and it's still developing. There are training links now with South Africa, and the UK military has become involved in providing trainers and gaining valuable experience for its personnel at the same time.

The whole enterprise is two way and respectful, and both countries get something out of it. And it builds goodwill and greater understanding between people from different countries.

***

The UK can teach but it can also learn from others. I asked Mark Britnell, global chair of health for KPMG and an expert on health systems globally, which countries the UK should be learning from.

He pointed me to Singapore, South Korea and the Scandinavian countries that have made health a priority not just for their own people but also as part of their nations' overall economic programmes. Health and prosperity go hand in hand in multiple ways. Healthy people are more productive, the biosciences can create competitive advantage in a modern economy, and health is one of the fastest-growing sectors globally. Expertise in health is also, as many countries have found in the Covid-19 pandemic, a great asset in international diplomacy, building goodwill and cultivating potential allies.

We talked about the way the Scandinavian countries addressed health as well as health services. They have largely led the way in *Health in All Policies*. This is an approach to public policies across sectors that systematically takes account of the health implications of decisions in all areas of policy, seeks synergies, and avoids harmful health impacts in order to improve population health and health equity.

This powerful approach started to gain traction during the Finnish Presidency of the European Union in 2006, and was most recently set out in the Helsinki statement on Health in All Policies in 2013. It follows on from earlier initiatives, including the Alma Ata Declaration on primary healthcare in 1978 and the Ottawa Charter for Health Promotion of 1986.

Finland is generally credited with one of the first projects to take this approach when, in 1972, it launched the North Karelia Project, with the aim of reducing coronary heart disease in the region by engaging other sectors, such as community organisations, dairy and meat producers, and schools, to improve community health. It resulted in significant reductions in cardiovascular disease mortality and was a very successful model for further cross-sector collaboration.

These are very important developments in government policy, which will undoubtedly become increasingly prominent in the years to come. They will be discussed further when we look at government in Chapter 15.

These approaches are all examples of seeking to make change through politics and public policy. More top down than bottom up. We can also learn from lower income countries, which may not have these policy frameworks and, if they do, often lack the means to implement them. They rely more on community action and courageous individuals. Bottom up. Taking control of their health and their communities. And sometimes, of course, going against public policy and received wisdom.

***

I have learned a great deal over the years from Professor Miriam Were. Miriam set up the first community health worker programmes in Kenya in the late 1970s and 80s and is one of the initiators of the whole movement across Africa.

As a medical student, Miriam realised that much of the illness she saw was due to the way people lived and what she described as *'the oral faecal link'*. The underlying problems were poor sanitation, dirty drinking water and the lack of the most basic health education. Infections spread easily and many patients were severely weakened by continuous bouts of illness and diarrhoea.

Today, there are a million or more community health workers. Most are village women who have been trained to do perhaps 20 tasks. Half these interventions are preventive, such as ensuring people use clean water for cooking or, perhaps, advising on family planning. The other half are curative; for example, helping mothers to rehydrate their children after diarrhoea. Community health workers can make an enormous contribution at the most local level and in the most remote areas.

Miriam was way ahead of her time, a true pioneer, in promoting community participation in health in 1970s Kenya. She was mocked by colleagues as *'the professor of latrines'*. It wasn't how they expected a doctor to behave. Years later she went on to lead her country's fight against HIV/AIDS and became chancellor of a university. She is now a highly respected figure nationally and globally.

Ten years ago, City Health Works, an organisation in New York, started running programmes to reach some of the most vulnerable people in the city, including addicts and homeless people who never used health services except in an emergency. City Health Works acknowledged explicitly copying the approach of African community health workers. The same principles applied about employing local people, working with the local culture and focusing on local issues – even if those issues were very different from the African experience.

Community is very important in the countries of Africa. Uche Amazigo, a scientist from Nigeria, and her colleagues used the strength of community ties to tackle river blindness or onchocerciasis. The disease is contracted in rivers from the larvae of a fly. Not long ago it had blinded most of the adults in some villages in parts of Africa.

River blindness is now in retreat and has already been eliminated in some countries by treating whole communities with a drug, ivermectin, which had been developed for de-worming dogs. One dose of the drug given once a year to everyone in a village for ten years is enough to protect them. The pharmaceutical company Merck has pledged to supply the drug free of charge for *'as long as it takes'* and NGOs such as Sightsavers manage its national distribution.

But the biggest problem was how to get the drug to everyone, even in the most far-flung areas. Uche and her colleagues developed and tested a workable methodology and spent several years implementing it across the affected countries. It involves tens of thousands of local volunteers visiting every household in their village, giving everyone the drug, recording the fact, and reporting back up the line to a country co-ordinator. It is impressive and well executed to a standard and consistency that would please any Western country employing professional staff to carry out a mass immunisation of its citizens. It is all about communities and volunteers.

Meanwhile, Mothers to Mothers (M2M) helps mothers in working together to stop the spread of HIV to their unborn children. It employs

1800 women living with HIV as mentor mothers, who help pregnant women with HIV adhere to protocols and safe practices, as well as providing emotional support. M2M works in several southern African countries and describes its work as all about *'women using shared experiences to create health and hope for other women and families in their communities'*.

There are many other schemes that engage community members and families in the different countries of Africa. In many places, this is simply the natural way of doing things. And sometimes it is the only way, because it is estimated that there are up to a billion people across the world who never see a health professional.

These sorts of approaches are used in other countries too. I visited the late Sir Fazle Abed, the founder of BRAC in Bangladesh. The organisation was set up in 1974 to meet the needs of refugees and the ultra-poor in the country at the end of the war of independence from Pakistan. I recall asking him what was the key to reducing the rates of child and maternal mortality in his country. *'Empower the women,'* he said. And BRAC was doing just that: educating village women and providing support for their livelihoods through micro-finance, as well as offering more conventional health services. And it was working, with truly impressive results, particularly in lower levels of child and infant deaths.

I don't want to paint too positive, romantic or, even, patronising a picture of health and healthcare in Africa or Bangladesh. I have seen corruption in several countries and, on occasion, political violence, and I have witnessed a great deal of suffering and poverty. But I also don't want to reproduce the clichéd picture of Africa as a continent enmired in problems and forever dependent on the charity of others. Africa consists of 54 countries and has a land mass equivalent to China, India, the contiguous USA and most of Europe put together, and generalisations about Africa are often facile or absurd.

The African experience is far more nuanced and there are many differences between countries. Problems remain, the population is growing unsustainably fast, and climate change will affect Africa perhaps more than any other continent. However, profound change is underway, there are growing numbers of well-educated people, increasing entrepreneurial activity, and we can expect to see Africa's economy and influence growing in the coming years. What's more, Africans will introduce many innovations and new approaches from which we can all learn.

The relationship between African countries and their aid donors and development partners is often very problematic. There is a division globally between high income countries, which make the rules, and the low and middle income countries, which have to accept them. The rule makers and the rule takers. This is about power and is still, to a considerable extent, influenced by the legacy of imperialism and colonialism, as well as the continued exploitation of resources and people.

The prejudices inherent in this relationship mean that we miss out on learning. Dr Matt Harris of Imperial College has shown that western countries and their institutions and scientific journals largely ignore innovations from Africa and the South. Even when dealing with innovative pharmaceuticals and repurposing drugs, which are so central to western scientific medicine. His work shows how important it is to understand the past and the roots of our own prejudices and preconceptions, and how these may be carried forward in the way in which we perceive and describe the world and the impact we may have on others.

The simple point here is that there are many skilled and committed people in low and middle income countries around the world who are finding new ways to create health. And there is so much we can learn from them about the involvement of communities, the role of women, the prevention of disease, the importance of innovation, and of breaking out of the straitjacket of received wisdom and accepted practice. Breaking the rules and taking control.

***

Professor Ged Byrne, director of global engagement at Health Education England, has been instrumental in transferring some of these ideas and learning into the NHS in England.

Ged is a surgical oncologist and has himself been a volunteer in partnership schemes in Africa. This experience inspired him to set up the Uganda UK Health Alliance with the aim of promoting collaboration between UK and Uganda based organisations working in health. The Alliance enables UK organisations working in Zambia to maximise their impact by linking them to other agencies working in the same geographical region or sharing similar activities, and by providing links to the Ugandan Ministry of Health.

The Alliance, which Ged chairs jointly with the Ugandan minister of health, has led to a range of improvements in services in Uganda, in areas as diverse as eyecare and mental health, and it has a main focus in the more remote North of the country. It has also supported many UK professionals to work in the country for both short and long periods.

Ged is very aware as an educator just how important this sort of experience can be in the training of health professionals, and he believes that all health professionals should learn about global health and have the opportunity to do part of their training, or at least gain experience, in another country. Through his role in Health Education England he has set up a number of exchange schemes where UK doctors and nurses spend some time abroad, and he is leading the implementation of extensive 'earn, learn and return' schemes for nurses from low and middle income countries.

Jamaica is one country to have such a scheme in place, following a request from the Jamaican Minister of Health Chris Tufton. It involves a group of nurses working in St James's Hospital in Leeds (earning), learning about intensive care, and who will return to Jamaica in three years' time. Large numbers of Indian nurses are also now involved in similar schemes elsewhere in England.

The UK and other richer countries have for years gained from the migration of health workers from poorer countries. The only solution in the long term must be for the UK and other benefitting countries to invest in training more health workers in these poorer countries, recognising their debt, and helping them train more of their own people at home. At the same time, the sending nations need to improve the pay and conditions in their own countries. For now, these sorts of agreed and well-organised circular migration schemes are beneficial both to the sending country and to the UK.

At the time of writing, there are growing fears in Africa that the pandemic will lead to renewed recruitment of health workers by the richer countries of the North, and that, as noted earlier, the global economic situation will reduce development support and reverse some of the gains of recent years.

The UK has been very active in many global health campaigns, including the current one on mental health and in leading advocacy on international issues, such as the importance of tackling the spread of antimicrobial resistance or drug resistant infections. But there are also concerns that the pandemic is leading to more competition for health resources and less co-operation, and that this will affect action on these vital issues in the future.

These worrying global trends will be discussed further in Chapter 16.

***

In 2016, the All-Party Parliamentary Group on Global Health, which I co-chair, published a review of nursing globally, the *Triple Impact of Nursing*. It highlighted that nurses make up more than half the health professional workforce globally yet, in large part because they are mostly women, they are undervalued and too often unable to use their training to the full and realise their potential. Nurses are still too often seen as hand maidens for doctors in some parts of the world. This is an extraordinary waste of talent and resources.

The *Triple Impact* report argued that we need to do much more to invest in, develop and support nurses, and that this would have the triple impact of improving health, promoting gender equity and strengthening local economies. Nurses are central to every health system, yet there is a global shortage.

The report was well received by nurses, but the UK's and other governments and the big donors we approached were simply not interested. They all said nice things about nurses, of course, but nurses simply weren't seen as significant enough or as having a big enough impact. And they weren't around the board tables, on the global commissions or involved in policy and decision making. They had difficulty making their voice heard.

I consulted with a few colleagues around the world and together we decided to launch a campaign, Nursing Now, designed to *'improve health globally by raising the profile and status of nurses'*. It has been very successful. It started in February 2018 and by May 2020, there were 661 local groups in 122 countries, all of them independent and self-funding. This year, 2020, has been declared the Year of the Nurse and the Midwife, and 27,500 young nurses and midwives from more than 70 countries have taken part in a global development programme. Perhaps more importantly, several governments are investing in and developing their nurses. All this has been achieved with a small budget and a staff equivalent to six full-time personnel.

The World Health Organization published the *State of the World's Nursing 2020* report in April 2020. This report, written jointly with Nursing Now and the International Council of Nurses, is the first ever country by country analysis of the nursing workforce globally. It shows that there is a global nursing workforce of 28 million, of whom 19 million are professionally trained, and that there is a shortfall of at least 6 million. Not surprisingly, the biggest shortfalls are concentrated in the poorest countries.

The Nursing Now campaign will be fully written up after it finishes in June 2021, but it is worth noting here a few preliminary lessons. It is vision led not plan led. Groups sign up to its vision, values and aims. But there is no standard plan or format that countries should follow and the campaign is not promoting a British, American or any other model of nursing. Countries know their own priorities. Nursing in Papua New Guinea is necessarily different from nursing in Canada. The campaign is not competing with anyone and welcomes all willing partners. And it is run in association with the two relevant democratic bodies: the World Health Organization and the International Council of Nurses.

Nursing Now is also open and transparent with an appropriate governance structure. Its board is made up of two thirds nurses and one third non-nurses; two thirds are women, one third are men, and it has representatives from young nurses and from all the regions of the world. Perhaps most importantly, it is about global solidarity, coming together to improve health, advocating change, and sharing and learning together.

These are all attributes of successful bottom-up advocacy and change. They are not about throwing millions of pounds or dollars at a problem – which can just mean buying support for a campaign – but about issues directly owned by supporters.

And nursing, I believe, will be a growth point for the future of health systems globally. Nurses will do much more and with more autonomy in the future, playing a much bigger part as – pandemics aside – populations develop more long term and chronic conditions, and more services move to the community and the home. They will, as one definition of nursing has it, *'walk alongside their patients'*.

Nurses with their values-driven and holistic view of health are well equipped to walk alongside us, guiding and supporting us, as we take control of our health and our communities.

Today, nurses are very visibly at the frontline in the fight against the pandemic and some, sadly, are dying. I don't believe anyone in the future will be able credibly to doubt their professionalism and skill and the value they bring to every area of health: from providing advice and comfort to employing the most advanced technical skills in intensive care and theatre.

UK Prime Minister Boris Johnson spoke movingly of the care nurses gave him while in intensive care, constantly present and working with compassion and skill. As one nurse from Canada said: *'At last, a world leader who understands what nursing is about.'*

His support will be vital in transforming these words into investment and action.

***

The pandemic, far from making us more insular with regard to health, should reinforce the importance of global solidarity and shared action.

Many people in the UK already well understand the importance of global action. THET, Health Education England, the *Lancet* and many other leading British organisations are already showing the way in emphasising that all health is global now.

This chapter leads to two final policy proposals for government. The first is that the Government should *convert its international development strategy into a co-development one, adopting the principles described here and, perhaps, renaming the Department for International Development as the Department for Global Development.*

The second recognises that the UK can play an enormous role in improving – and creating – health globally. It has deep expertise and remarkable networks and relationships worldwide. The UK has world class universities and research, is a global leader in health policy and international development, has strong life sciences and biomedical and biotech industries, and has a vibrant and diverse not for profit sector.

The UK is already a world leader in health and should give this role even greater priority: *planning for the country to become a truly global centre for health and health science.*

PART THREE

THE NEW PARTNERSHIP – HEALTH CREATION, THE NHS AND GOVERNMENT

CHAPTER THIRTEEN

THE BIG IDEAS

The earlier chapters show us a different way of thinking about health, which puts the emphasis on creating health rather than on treating disease and trauma.

Both, of course, are important. The NHS has a vital role to play in treating and managing disease and trauma, and it can become even more effective in the future by transforming from a hospital based system to one focused on the community with a new emphasis on health and prevention, not just on illness and disease. The response to Covid-19 appears to be strengthening and accelerating this transformation with more consultations being done remotely.

Government, too, can do far more to create health and prevent disease by developing positive health and life-enhancing education, employment, economic and environmental policies, devolving responsibilities and strengthening local communities.

And the UK is a global leader in health and health science. In every area: from research to professional education, from biotech to health services and international development. It can become even stronger in the future as a truly global centre for health and health science.

However, the NHS and government can't do it all by themselves. They need to work with and alongside today's health creators in an approach that unites health creation with service delivery and wider government policy. It is this combination of health creation, the NHS and government that can really make a difference to our health and wellbeing and establish a new post-industrial approach to health and health systems.

This chapter brings together the ten big ideas from earlier chapters that underpin the whole health-creating approach and can make it a reality. The following two chapters describe what this means for the NHS and for government, respectively.

The final two chapters put all this in the context of the wider changes happening in the world and end with a call to action.

1. Take off our NHS spectacles and leave behind our preconceptions and prejudices

The first big idea is that we need to take off our NHS spectacles and think about health differently. It is very easy to assume that the way we do things now is the natural or only way to do them. Or that what worked well in the past will work well in the future. Or that health professionals and the health system always know best. And we do this unconsciously, without thinking about it.

Health is made at home asks us to think differently about people as well as ideas. We all have our unconscious biases and prejudices. As the earlier chapters show, we can learn from people living on benefits in a Manchester housing estate or people in rural Africa, as well as from the greatest clinicians and scientists of our day. They each have a different vantage point on the world and have different insights to share.

My journey started in Africa precisely because there is so much that we in the UK can learn from people without our resources and who don't share our preconceptions about health and health systems.

We need constantly to challenge our own ideas.

2. Talk about mental health

We all need to talk about mental health. And anyone – friends, neighbours, employers, trades unions and teachers – can start the conversation. It is something we can all do something about.

Western medicine has traditionally focused on the physical and biological; body systems and physical disease processes. And our mental health service has grown up over the years to become a largely separate system. There is some coming together around the neurosciences and psychiatry but, for the most part, minds and bodies are treated by different people and in different ways.

A 2012 Act of Parliament required the NHS to give mental health equal status – *parity of esteem* – with physical health but barriers and stigma persist, and there is still too little investment in mental health and very little integration of services.

Now mental illness, stress, anxiety and depression are recognised as the biggest health issues in the workplace and, as so many of the stories in this book show, mental and physical health go hand in hand at all stages of life, from childhood to parenting and old age. And in every context, from school and the workplace, to home and the community. It is already clear that the Covid-19 pandemic and the ensuing lockdown have increased mental health problems dramatically and that the consequences will be long lasting and very damaging.

Many professionals, especially nurses, already adopt a biopsychological perspective on health, seeking to understand physical and mental health issues alongside each other. Some are going further still, bringing in the societal and environmental issues to offer a more rounded or holistic view of health and wellbeing and of the needs of each individual. The systems now need to copy these professionals.

And we can all start the conversation.

3. Focus on relationships

Cranbury College has a relationship policy not a behavioural one. It is about how people relate to each other and not about individual behaviour. Adults at the College and at Path Hill Farm work to create a relationship with children excluded from school, giving them a safe and trusted space to question and experiment. We are all shaped or distorted, enabled or disabled by our relationships.

And it's the same with organisations. Things get done when people from different organisations know each other, build relationships, create trust and find creative ways of working together. Things don't get done when people with the same job titles – social services directors, head teachers, chief executives or police superintendents – act out their individual roles, guard their territory, and keep others at a distance.

I learned in the NHS that relationships and culture always trump structure and strategy. And that leaders who could build relationships with others from different backgrounds were best able to achieve even the most difficult things.

Structure, systems, discipline and planning matter but there needs to be much more emphasis on relationships and culture at every stage of planning and delivery – in business, creating an organisation, delivering public services, and working with the public and patients.

It is not surprising that where this doesn't happen people talk about getting things done *despite* the system.

4. Build on strengths

Encourage aspiration. Help people find something at which they can succeed. Recognise talent. Understand differences. Build on strengths. Become a taxpayer! And ignore those who tell you that you're a failure.

This is the most obvious big idea of them all. But it's not generally how our society is organised. Our lives are full of rules and tests – particularly for children – and we focus too much on disabilities and dependency rather than abilities, contributions and potential.

Commercial marketing as well as popular culture reinforce these processes, encouraging conformity, limiting imagination and reinforcing stereotypes. There are other strengths that don't fit these patterns and which we too easily ignore.

We lose out as individuals and as a nation. With children failing in academic courses when they could succeed in vocational ones, nurses unable to work to their full potential, and people who are different in some way written off through conscious or unconscious bias.

How many of us would be like Heather Henry and see the unemployed fathers of a Salford housing state as a hidden strength, not a problem? They didn't even see themselves that way.

We need to identify strengths and nurture them.

5. Recognise the importance of communities

Most of us belong to one or more communities, however we choose to define them: geographically, ethnically or in any other way.

Our health as individuals is closely linked to the health of our communities. They can give us strength and identity, promote healthy relationships, offer us safety and security, and enhance our health and our lives. Or they can do the opposite, promoting division, an echo chamber for our own bitterness and despair, harming our health, and limiting our aspirations.

Austerity has damaged many local communities in the UK, shredding their infrastructure, helping create in some places a strong sense of alienation, and strengthening existing subcultures of addiction, gangs and crime. Rebuilding them and creating a positive sense of place where people can thrive are vital. Places where, for example, police officers and supermarket managers won't be criticised for helping young people to create and run a dance school.

Our health and the health of our communities and wider society go hand in hand.

6. Have a meaning and purpose in life

People of all ages need a meaning and purpose in life. When we are younger it can drive our passion to compete and excel, to change the world, or to follow our vocation as a nurse or teacher, or indeed a parent.

And it becomes more important as we grow older when we no longer have to face the constant pressures of education, parenting or working. Older age can be a time of freedom and opportunity; of leisure and learning. But it's not always like this. It is also for many a time of insecurity and poverty, loneliness and despair.

The arts can play a vital role. The women's group in Bolton chose art as their reason to meet. For others it's dance, joining an art class or the great communal experience of singing in a choir. Phil Freeman used plays, music and humour as a teacher to help his students think through some of the issues they were interested in – sex and relationships, politics, the environment.

Creativity is good in itself, using a different part of the brain and releasing beneficial chemicals. And it's also good for building communities, creating relationships, revealing hidden strengths, reducing stress, and bringing people out of themselves.

And whatever that meaning and purpose may be, it can enhance health and wellbeing and guard against loneliness, depression and feelings of worthlessness. It can even, if we need it to, provide a reason for living.

And we also need others to respect our meaning and purpose – recognising our strengths and potential contribution – and not just treat us as helpless, dependent and in need of care.

7. Connect and communicate

Most of the success stories in this book depend on people making connections between ideas and between people and organisations.

Much of this is simply about bringing people together to create a sense of solidarity and shared interest, and to spark ideas and develop creative solutions. The first thing that the City Mental Health Alliance did was to invite people to a meeting to discuss mental health, share their experiences and think together about the way forward. The Salford Dadz evolved from men having the chance to meet, talk and plan activities. Men in Sheds is about reconnecting men who have become isolated with other people.

Part of this is also about mutual learning and co-development: each individual or group bringing something different to the table, learning and growing together. The Incredible Edible groups around the country learn from each other and so do the different forest schools. And the partnerships between British and African hospitals, with their very different circumstances and vastly different resources, are all two way with each gaining from working with the other.

Organisations, too, need to work together and communicate better. The NHS working with local authorities, public bodies and private businesses, schools and the community: each bring their own expertise, approach and perspective. And there needs to be more sharing of ideas and insights about health and community, employment, education and the environment, as well as using shared concepts such as place and sustainability, co-production and community assets.

Connecting and communicating are the essential starting points.

8. The environment matters

Healthy people need healthy communities and a healthy environment. Our own experience teaches us and science confirms that a healthy environment and the natural world enhance our health and wellbeing.

Well-designed buildings and communities, and access to natural light, greenery and fresh air are all important, whether in our own homes or in a stressful environment such as a removal centre or prison. Being able to see greenery from your hospital bed raises the spirits, and Horatio's Gardens are valued by their users as places to escape from the clinical environment, release stress and breathe freely.

There is a bigger picture, too, the health of the planet: climate change, the destruction of the natural environment and the ravages of pollution all impact negatively on our health and wellbeing. Many of the same factors that harm our health – from air pollution, transport systems and sedentary lifestyles, to unhealthy farming methods, food processing and animal husbandry – also damage the environment.

Our health depends on a healthy planet as well as on healthy communities and a healthy society.

9. Be entrepreneurial, experiment and learn by doing

There are many business and social entrepreneurs in this book: Jamie Burrows and Vertical Future; Paula Gamester and the Sewing Rooms;

and Lord John Bird with *The Big Issue*, for example. They have all learned by doing. Lord Andrew Mawson and colleagues didn't set out 30 years ago to build a joined-up neighbourhood. They learned by experimentation, with one thing leading to another. Richard Howells didn't have the whole plan for Tribe in his head. And while the Nursing Now campaign was launched with a vision and set of aims, it has taken opportunities, many of them unanticipated, as they have arisen.

This learning by doing has not only produced beneficial results but has also ensured that the people implementing these programmes and projects own their work and are motivated to keep improving. There are now systematic methods for improvement used successfully in some parts of industry and the public sector that rely on testing out incremental changes, paying attention to the detail, and refining their plans in response to the results. And, of course, this is how the scientific method works.

These approaches are very different from what is still the normal practice in the NHS and other public services, where processes of business planning, target setting and measurement have been painfully learned in recent years. While these are all important methods and have their place, they can stifle creativity and delay feedback and learning if applied too rigidly. Particularly when accompanied by burdensome methods of accountability, monitoring and inspection.

The uncertainty of today's rapidly changing environment means that it is more important than ever to be creative and to test ideas out. This is new territory for us all and the only way forward is experimentation and learning by doing.

10. Take control

Autonomy and control are central to creating health. As Hazel Stuteley says, improved health – or health creation – comes from individuals and communities having a sense of mastery and control over their lives and environment.

At the personal and community level this is about confidence, owning the issues, throwing off any vestiges of helplessness and dependence, and taking action. It can require great courage, particularly when people are feeling vulnerable. It is also about vision, determination and a degree of self-discipline in everything from physical activity to diet.

More generally, it is about advocating and pressing for change in wider society. Our ability to be truly healthy depends on many factors, from education and the welfare system, to employment and environmental protection. We need to be able to influence them.

And personal autonomy, taking control for ourselves, is good for our health and wellbeing.

***

Taken together, these ten big ideas describe a new health-creating approach, which is very different from the traditional government and NHS one of structure and systems, siloed approaches and professional boundaries, and their cautious top-down planning and focus on illness and problems.

The implications for the NHS and government are explored in the next two chapters.

There is a new narrative emerging that is about healthy individuals in healthy communities, a healthy society and healthy planet. It is about creating health and the conditions for people to be healthy. And there are roles for everyone to play alongside the NHS and government.

Health is made at home and in the workplace, the school and the community. Hospitals are for repairs.

CHAPTER FOURTEEN

WHAT THIS MEANS FOR THE NHS

The health creators, the NHS and government need to work together as partners in creating and improving health, each bringing something different to the enterprise.

This chapter looks at what some of the leading-edge organisations in the NHS are doing to make this happen and suggests how this could be accelerated.

The NHS has been forced to change some of its policies and practices in response to the pandemic with, most obviously, far greater use of virtual consultations and the involvement of thousands of volunteers in the community. It has also given greater impetus to technological and service innovation. There is the opportunity to maintain and build on the best of these changes after the crisis, but success will depend on there being the necessary will to change and on some fundamental shifts in behaviours and attitudes.

Devolution has meant that the NHS and many other public services have evolved differently in each of the four countries of the United Kingdom, and these next two chapters deal only with the English NHS and government policy in England. All references to the NHS mean the English NHS.

***

How should the NHS respond to these new ways of thinking about health with their broader approach to the social and economic determinants of health and their insistence on the importance of people being in control?

How can health professionals work with the health pioneers with their wide range of activities and their different backgrounds and behaviours?

And how can the great scientific enterprise of the NHS engage with a seemingly softer and more subjective approach built on concepts such as relationships, meaning, community and learning by doing?

They seem to be worlds apart. The NHS, however, has many of the characteristics of a social movement. Something people belong to and are passionate about. Many of the roots of the NHS are in local community hospitals, workers' co-operative movements and a sense of social justice. It grew up in a time when people demanded better for themselves and their families. It would be, in the words of principal founder Aneurin Bevan: *'In place of fear'*.

As a leaflet sent to every household in June 1948 explained: *'It will provide you with all medical, dental and nursing care. Everyone – rich or poor, man, woman or child – can use it or any part of it. There are no charges, except for a few special items. There are no insurance qualifications. But it is not a 'charity'. You are all paying for it, mainly as tax payers, and it will relieve your money worries in time of illness.'* It was created in place of fear.

There have been many changes over the years, but this sense of common purpose, shared values and social justice still inspires most health professionals, is written into government policy and attracts very wide public support.

And as this chapter will show, there are many people inside and outside the NHS who are trying to make the connections work – attempting to align the 'national' of the NHS with the 'local' of the community. And NHS policy is shifting, with a new focus on integrated local working and on tackling the wider determinants of health.

***

There are three fundamental problems that make it difficult for the NHS to respond effectively to the health creators. It was designed to tackle very different diseases and conditions. It was created for a different time and culture. And there is an enormous baggage of history and vested interests, which mean change of almost any kind is always resisted by someone.

Today's major diseases require different types of services from those needed in the 1940s. Much of the care needed then was acute and episodic in nature, one-off events of treatment and (hopefully) cure. Now, much of the care is for recurring and long term conditions. Then, clinicians were mainly dealing with single conditions or problems. Now, many patients have multiple conditions, which need different treatments from each other. And in 1948, most cancers were fairly rapid killers. Now, most are long term conditions and their treatment is complicated by other diseases or co-morbidities.

The NHS that developed in the 1940s was also shaped by the culture, technology and political manoeuvrings of the day. The result, as noted in Chapter 2, is a system where doctors and hospitals are dominant, the focus is on treatment not prevention, and there are organisational and cultural divides between specialities, between secondary and primary care, and between the NHS and social care.

This segmentation is very difficult for patients who may need services from different specialities and organisations and may require support from social care as well as the NHS. And precisely the same sorts of issues arise when outside organisations try to work as partners with the NHS. Who can a housing association such as Bolton at Home work with? Who is going to be able to respond to the ideas of Incredible Edible? And who has the authority to enable the Tribe Project, which has implications for both the NHS and local authorities, to spread rapidly across the country?

It is a simple fact of life that organisations set up for one purpose find it very difficult to adapt to serve another. Almost everything has to change. What might sound like a relatively straightforward redesign of a service may well run up against professional demarcations about who does what, financial problems – with only certain types of services being paid for – confidentiality of data issues, and organisational boundaries about who does what or who pays for what. And underlying them may be questions about job security, the future viability of organisations and, even, private practice.

The third problem area is all about power and money and overt or covert resistance to change from those with vested interests in the status quo – and there are many of these, from the great hospital institutions, which retain enormous power and influence, to pharma and other suppliers, the professional bodies and, of course, the politicians.

This critique applies to the health systems in every developed country. They are all trapped in 20th century models and all striving to break out and find new ways of working appropriate to the conditions and diseases of the 21st century.

The greater paradox, hidden in plain sight, is that so much of the gain in health since 1948 has come from outside the health system in areas such as sanitation, education, economic growth and legislation.

Nevertheless, there is substantial change happening in the NHS. The 2019 NHS Long Term Plan, designed to make the NHS fit for the future, explicitly refers to giving patients more control over their own health and care and to promoting *integrated care systems* and *sustainability and transformation partnerships*, both of which bring NHS and other bodies together around shared goals. It also has preventing illness and tackling health inequalities as one of its main strategy areas.

This plan and the Pathfinder programmes established earlier have both encouraged a great deal of experimentation and learning, which are starting to show how the traditional top-down approach from the NHS can begin to engage with the bottom-up health creation efforts of the health pioneers.

The focus in this book is entirely on how these NHS organisations can work with the health creators. It doesn't attempt to deal with the myriad other NHS issues such as service delivery, staffing, organisation, funding, quality, governance and technology, each of which are the subject of other, far longer books.

***

New NHS Alliance, despite its name, is not part of the NHS and works across other professional sectors such as housing and social care, as well as health. Merron Simpson, its chief executive, describes it as a *'movement for health creation and action on health inequalities'* and says its focus is on *'changing the dynamic of the relationship between health and other professionals and the communities they work in'*.

The Alliance defines health creation as *'a route to wellness. It comes about when local people and professionals work together as equal partners and focus on what matters to people and their communities.'* Its membership reflects this ambition, with people from different local communities working alongside professionals, researchers, policy analysts and innovators, who understand that health is a social process and who see health creation as a way to enable individuals and communities to improve their health.

The Alliance centres its work around the question *'what makes people well?'* This has led it to conclude that, to be well and stay well, people need sufficient levels of the three Cs: control, contact and confidence, by which it means: *'Control over the circumstances of their lives and the things that affect them. Contact with other people that is enjoyable, meaningful and purposeful. Confidence to see themselves as an asset able to have a positive impact on their own and others' lives.'*

'There is increasing evidence that the three Cs are very important in making and keeping people well,' Merron told me, *'including from academics who inform Public Health England and who have spoken at our events. There is now enough evidence to act.'*

The Alliance has developed a set of five *'health-creating practices'*, which describe how professionals need to act in partnership with local people to create health. Health professionals are very powerful people and with the best will in the world can fail to respond to the concerns of the public, hold back on unpalatable truths, or inadvertently get in the way of people organising themselves. As was discussed in Chapter 12, local people generally know what needs doing and want the professionals to help them to do it – not tell them what to do.

The practices all came from listening to local people about what made them well. I think they are extraordinarily valuable and are quoted in full here with the permission of the Alliance. They are:

'**Listening and responding**: *Effective, genuine listening to the reality of people's and communities' lives is essential. As is acting differently upon what is heard, and not just reverting to the established systems. Listening can also help to build trust that enables truth-telling if people feel safe to open up about matters they might be hiding, even from themselves. Being listened to can also be therapeutic in itself.*

'**Truth-telling**: *When people and practitioners identify and acknowledge what holds them back from creating health, rather than treating illness, they can start to get to the root causes of problems and solutions. This can be a challenge to the system because it is not set up to create health through a social process.*

'**Strengths focus**: *Health creation happens when attention is paid to what people can do for themselves or others. Making people aware of their strengths and finding opportunities for them to employ them unlocks their potential and builds confidence for creating health.*

'**Self-organising**: *Helping people to connect meaningfully with others makes it possible for them to find solutions and take actions together. They are more likely to find purpose in their lives and this drives wellness. Over time, people become less reliant on health and care services.*

'**Power-shifting**: *Lasting health creation happens when the health-creating features above result in a power shift from practitioners to people and communities. When people's expertise and strengths are recognised and valued, they can make good decisions, take action and have an influence over things that affect them and their environment. Services can then adapt and respond accordingly.*'

These seem to me to be very important practices – almost a code of practice for the future. They are particularly important in a world where consultation with the public can often seem, and sometimes is, token and has no real impact. And where people living in a community often have very little control over resources and how they are spent.

The Alliance was originally a voice for primary care dominated by GPs but it has been through a transformation, starting in early 2016, to reflect what it saw as the new needs of a changing environment. It plans to follow this through by changing its name to *National Health Creation Alliance* from 2021 so as to reflect more accurately what it actually does.

Despite having very little resource, the Alliance is now regularly consulted by the NHS and the Department for Health and Social Care on how the NHS can work effectively with communities. It aims to influence through events, resources and publications, and Merron believes that, as a result, health creation is beginning to be understood more widely both locally and nationally.

I asked Merron whether these health-creating practices were spreading throughout the NHS and beyond. She told me that people respond well to the concepts and are able to see how they relate to their own work and identify gaps in their practice. Different sectors, both within and outside the NHS, respond differently. She told me that organisations tend to be strong on one or more of the five features of health-creating practices, but few are strong on all five.

Two of the practices – community self-organising and power-shifting – are the hardest for practitioners to adopt because of the loss of power. Yet, these are probably the most important. They enable communities to be stronger, more self-sufficient and less reliant on health and care services. The Covid-19 crisis demonstrates that communities with higher levels of organisation and connections have been able to respond most effectively, and with fewer people isolated.

The Alliance is currently working through its future options and thinking about where it can best add value. I came away from my conversation with Merron with a strong sense that it could play a significant role in changing the way health professionals work in the community. It is how people work and the mindset they bring to the task that seems to me to be the most important point. The how. Not the principles, but the relationships – and the listening, the truth-telling, the strengths focus, the self-organising and the power-shifting.

Other bodies are also working in this and related areas. In recent years, the idea of co-production between the public and professional workers has become widespread in the public sector. Definitions vary but this generally covers the engagement of citizens in the conception, design and management of public services, and also the embracing of professional behaviours and approaches.

Within the NHS, for example, the Coalition for Collaborative Care and the Ideas Alliance have worked with NHS England to produce *The art of co-production* – a guerrilla guide, which offers practical advice and provides examples of what has worked. The Health Foundation and NHS Horizons, among others, are also contributing to a better understanding of what is possible.

There is a danger, of course, that co-production can just slip back into the professionals telling people what to do, co-opting patients and citizens to their cause. This is why the Alliance's *health-creating practices* are so important – they change the relationship.

***

These are not the only approaches. One of the best known health and community initiatives in England, the Bromley by Bow Centre, grew up one step at a time, learning by doing as its founders saw new needs and opportunities in front of them. There were no tool kits, case studies or best practices to follow when it started 35 years ago.

I described the Centre briefly in Chapter 8. It is an entrepreneurial hub for activities of all sorts and focused physically around the church, where Lord Andrew Mawson arrived as a young non-conformist minister in 1984, and the primary care practice. The practice was established by Andrew and colleagues in 1997 after a long struggle, which was only resolved when the then Secretary of State for Health, Dr Brian Mawhinney, personally intervened.

The Centre has been visited many times by government ministers and civil servants, as well as by clinicians and community leaders wanting to understand how it works and learn any lessons. It has become a model for the future of primary care and the NHS. Rob Trimble, who has been part of the development since 1990 and became the Centre's chief executive in 2002, explained that I should think of it as a sort of community department store. '*A John Lewis model*', he said.

It has four features. It is owned by the community through a charity. It is accessible by everyone. It emphasises customer service. And it offers a wide range of products and services.

The range of services – or departments in the department store – is impressive. Alongside health services, people can find classes of various sorts, sports activities, social groups, support for small enterprises – it has helped set up more than 50 social enterprises in local boroughs in the last nine years – and get help from social services and receive welfare and other advice. It has expanded over the years and the Centre now involves 87 businesses and four health centres across 30 sites in East London.

It is truly a centre of the community and I noticed that its own research on the impact of the Centre on local people began with the question *'what are the ingredients of a good life?'*

It's a telling point. This is not just about health. Health is part of something bigger. Rob emphasised that what they are doing is building a community where people look after each other. People may come in to see him with a problem and he will say *'Hang on, I'll put on a kettle.'* Making time to deal with it properly. Making people welcome. *'You have to build up trust,'* he says. *'Earn your credibility.'*

Rob says the whole Centre is focused around four active values, which are instilled in all employees: be compassionate, be a friend, have fun, assume it's possible.

And it is emphatically not about health professionals. Indeed, he says the whole thing falls down if the primary care professionals are seen as *'the custodians of health'*. And it didn't start with health but with the community: play groups, dancing classes, a meeting place for Bengali women and local businesses. Health, in the form of the primary care practice, was invited in.

Where New NHS Alliance is focused on how health professionals can work with local people, empowering and enabling them with their health-creating practices, Bromley by Bow is all about community, with health as a part – sometimes the main part and sometimes as a by-product of other activity – and the pursuit of the good life. Both examples offer us clear pointers for the future of the NHS.

I asked Rob what the future held for the Centre and was surprised to hear that he was worried about making the whole enterprise sustainable. Despite its success and the accolades from politicians and NHS leaders, they are finding it difficult to get the funding they need. Until the financial flows within the NHS change, it appears that these innovative models will struggle to survive and have to get by as best they can on short term project and programme money. And they have to spend far too much time fundraising.

***

Andrew Mawson went on to lead the St Paul's Way Transformation Project in 2006, which has reinvigorated and regenerated a run-down part of Tower Hamlets, and to play a leading role in the Olympics legacy programme, which was based very near the Centre and benefitted from its experience. He now chairs Well North Enterprises.

Each of these activities offer us a far bigger picture of the role that the NHS and health organisations can play in the wider development of communities – creating health in doing so but also making progress towards other social goals. Andrew sees the ultimate goal as being about transforming public services. With health alongside all the others.

Well North was set up in 2015 as a partnership between Public Health England, the University of Manchester and the Manchester Academic Health Science Centre. It was designed to work for three years with partners from local authorities, NHS organisations, businesses, and community, voluntary and faith organisations to find new ways of creating healthy communities in ten places in the North of England as Pathfinders or exemplars for the future. It made progress in all these areas.

Andrew subsequently set up Well North Enterprises in 2018 as a community interest company and legacy vehicle, which could build on these developments and provide support for businesses and public organisations around the country seeking to create healthy communities. It is currently engaged in many projects across the country.

Two examples of its projects are based respectively in Surrey in the South of England and Bradford in the North. Well North Enterprises is working with the Ashford and St Peter's Hospitals NHS Foundation Trust to broaden the Trust's role in the local community, using the redevelopment of one of the Trust's two major sites as an opportunity to create new facilities and meet the needs of the local community. It is also, Andrew stresses, rethinking what a hospital should be in the future.

The company is also engaged with Bradford Teaching Hospitals NHS Foundation Trust, the local authority, businesses and others to create a new health and wellness centre based on the lessons learned at Bromley by Bow. It is a much bigger development with sports and other facilities that will be built beside the main hospital and draw on its expertise and support. Andrew sees this as the opportunity to place health and wellbeing absolutely at the centre of the whole local community and local economy and, as in Surrey, help shape the future of health.

I talked with Lucinda McArthur, the former chief executive of Well North Enterprises, about Skelmersdale, one of the original ten Well North Pathfinders. Skelmersdale is a town of about 40,000 people who had mostly been moved from Liverpool as part of the redevelopment of the 1970s, and it has the high level of sickness and health problems you would expect of a relatively deprived area with high levels of unemployment. There isn't a hospital in the town and, until recently, there was nowhere you could study for your A levels.

The heritage, culture and history of its relationship with Liverpool comes through, Lucinda told me, even though the town is in rural Lancashire. *'And despite all the problems,'* she said, *'there's a real sense of community. Something special. A buzz.'*

There was something here for her and her colleagues to build on, a local will and determination. They set about developing and deepening relationships with the people of Skelmersdale. People who were local, who knew the town and who knew what made it 'tick'. They met with the different bodies in the town: the council, the NHS, the police, the college and the local businesses. Some had seen recent changes of leadership and new energy and ideas were being injected into their thinking. There were plans for redeveloping the town centre, which represented an opportunity for change.

There were also some very successful social enterprises. The Sewing Rooms, which was described in Chapter 7, employs local people as well as providing classes and social activity for anyone in the neighbourhood. Not far away is the Artz Centre, offering classes for adults and young people, working in schools, holding performances, and providing professional support for performing artists. Like other social enterprises, they both boost health and wellbeing alongside tackling other social issues and improving the local economy.

Lucinda told me that the vision was to create a connected community with the social, employment, educational and other links that would enable people to thrive. It was about relationships, mental health, meaning, building on strengths, and the other big issues discussed in the last chapter and, of course, the importance of community.

'*It was,*' she said, '*about investing in trust for the long term.*'

Jackie Moran, who works for the NHS locally, took up the story. She is the director of transformation and integration for NHS West Lancashire Clinical Commissioning Group and is driving the development of the West Lancashire Partnership, Multi-Speciality Community Provider Partnership, a new body which, as its cumbersome name implies, brings together all the key service providers across West Lancashire including Skelmersdale and the neighbouring village of Up Holland.

Jackie's task is really to help turn that trust into practical action that benefits the community. The fact that there isn't a hospital within the Partnership area means that Jackie and colleagues can concentrate on the social determinants of health – poverty, unemployment, education, housing, crime and all the other external societal issues that affect our health. The areas in fact where the health pioneers I have described in earlier chapters are creating health and wellbeing.

There are some practical difficulties, Jackie told me, in bringing the different partners together around the same agenda and in technical matters like the sharing of information, changing some rules and regulations, and the employment of staff. And she made it clear it is about relationships between people, not their job titles; people really have to buy into the reality of working together and not everyone does. And it's long term. Trust for the longer term. Longer term relationships.

Once the relationships are there, the opportunities will appear. It is noticeable that so many of the successful examples in this book are projects that have been developed over many years and often with the same core team. There is something here about determination and perseverance but also, I suspect, about proving your loyalty and commitment to local people. And these relationships have proved vital in managing the impact of the pandemic: places where there are well-established relationships appear to have fared better than those without them.

Jackie told me how in Skelmersdale they have concentrated on getting people into work and improving educational attainment with a firm focus on children. The health system has worked with the college to encourage children into learning about health and social care. They want to create a pipeline of children interested in the subjects, gaining qualifications at the college, and subsequently being employed by the NHS and local authorities in the area. There are real and obvious connections here. And health and social care, as we will discuss in Chapter 15, are growing areas of employment that will surely continue to expand as the whole job market changes.

I talked with both Lucinda and Jackie about how much of this activity in Skelmersdale was top down, as opposed to bottom up and community led. It's a very difficult balance. The authorities need to get their act together, break out of their silos and respond flexibly to local initiative. As Pam Warhurst of Incredible Edible said, both parties need to be involved. And where things work well is where the authorities are ready and able to play their part. *'Both hands clapping,'* as she put it.

Andrew Mawson makes another important point. It's not top down or bottom up, he told me, but inside out. Working from the inside. It's all about relationships and trust.

The Five Year Forward View and the Long Term Plan for the NHS introduced some experimental organisational arrangements, including these multi-speciality community partnerships, which could be tested out in different parts of the country. It is envisaged that, if these work well, the partnerships would eventually merge some or all of their budgets and management structures.

A far larger version of this approach has been underway in Greater Manchester since 2015 when the ten metropolitan boroughs, the mayor and local groups came together, in the words of their memorandum of understanding: *'(to) ensure the greatest and fastest possible improvement to the health and wellbeing of the 2.8 million citizens of Greater Manchester. This requires a more integrated approach to the use of the existing health and care resources – around £6bn in 2015-16 – as well as transformational changes in the way in which services are delivered across Greater Manchester.'*

Early evidence suggests that progress is being made with this ambitious goal. There is certainly a lot of creative thinking and action taking place locally in the Greater Manchester area, ranging from the Wigan Deal, which addresses the whole of the public realm in Wigan, to the smaller but important activities of Bolton at Home and Salford Dadz.

***

There are other organisations in the NHS that have been transforming themselves with or without external help over recent years.

Primary care is at the forefront of change and I discussed this with Sir Sam Everington. A GP, he worked with Andrew Mawson to move his primary care practice to the Bromley by Bow Centre in the 1990s. He has been involved in most of the developments in primary care since, from primary care groups to clinical commissioning groups and the many Pathfinder organisations. These developments have over the years brought GPs into a much more prominent and powerful role in planning services and managing NHS resources.

Sam became chair of the Tower Hamlets Clinical Commissioning Group at its formation in April 2013 when it took over responsibility for commissioning NHS services across the borough from the different NHS, private and not for profit providers. He now chairs the London

Clinical Commissioning Council, which brings together the chairs of the 32 clinical commissioning groups in London and provides oversight and support for their activities. It is an extremely influential position.

The Bromley by Bow Centre in partnership with Sam, Dr Julia Davies and the partners in their practice started social prescribing 17 years ago. There is now a large national movement, built on their work and that of other pioneers, where doctors and other clinicians refer people to activities in the community to improve their health and wellbeing. These might be dance or art classes, gardening, physical activity, befriending or volunteering schemes. Staff at the Bromley by Bow Centre, for example, help patients get involved in any of about 30 local services.

There is systematic evidence about the impacts of social prescribing and plenty of emerging and anecdotal evidence that it leads to improvements in mental and physical wellbeing, reduced levels of depression and anxiety, and improvements in the general quality of life. Some leading-edge organisations are now using it to tackle wider issues such as knife crime. There is also some evidence that it reduces the use of other services, such as A&E, and even reduces admissions. One project at the centre, called DIY health, reduced attendance in primary care and casualty by 35 per cent. It involved group sessions with parents and helping them to understand how to manage minor ailments.

Social prescribing is popular with participants, primary care professionals and commissioners and the NHS is promoting it heavily. NHS England has set up a national team led by a former chair of the Royal College of GPs, and funded the appointment of 1000 link workers to help practices place patients in community schemes.

I have, however, come across concerns from some of the people involved in community activities that social prescribing is distorting what they are doing. And they told me they were even receiving complaints from primary care practices that there weren't enough community activities available or that local activities were refusing referrals. As Heather Nelson pointed out in Chapter 11, the practices and the link workers were being paid for making referrals but the community activities weren't being paid for taking people on.

There is a paradox here. Why aren't the community activities funded directly so that people can use them and cut out the referral altogether? Especially as this would bring many other benefits in building up community infrastructure.

That is not entirely fair, of course, because many people might not be motivated to join the activity without the doctor or nurse prescribing it. However, it illustrates the point that building up community resources is not yet seen as good in itself but only where it serves another purpose.

I discussed these issues with Sam and asked him why it was called *social prescribing*. Didn't this just medicalise normal life? Sam understood this view but, he told me, they had decided to call it prescribing because it is a concept that doctors are familiar with, and it would encourage them to start doing it.

Sam went on to talk about the mutual addiction there is between doctors and their patients – both can become dependent on the other – and the importance of breaking this up. Social prescribing might be one route and strengthening the role of nurses could be another. Already, he told me, a significant percentage of elderly and chronically ill patients were managed by a multidisciplinary team led by a nurse.

In fact, he said, nurses could do about 80 per cent of what doctors currently do in primary care. Doctors, he said, had vital roles in leadership, training, 'risk holding' and developing the team, alongside using their clinical skills to treat patients; but so much more could be done by other people.

Nurses, as was discussed in Chapter 12, are part of the community they serve, understand its culture, provide continuity of care and are increasingly well educated. They will surely, as Sam suggests, play an increasingly major role in primary care and the management of patients with long term and chronic conditions. True to his principles, Sam's practice has a nurse partner. It is genuinely a primary care practice, not a GP one.

Sam also stressed the importance of the local communities growing their own health workers, in an echo of what Jackie Moran had said in Skelmersdale. He was worried about the increasing use of agency doctors. Good technical people maybe, but not the rounded health workers who know their community and their team.

The East London NHS Foundation Trust is another NHS body at the forefront of change that is helping point the way to the future. It runs mental health and community services with a turnover of about £450 million, split evenly between the two. It is one of the most successful trusts in the NHS, with high levels of staff and user satisfaction, meeting its service and financial targets, and rated 'outstanding' by the Care Quality Commission. Its mission and strategy are also very unusual.

The Trust's respective chief executive and chair, Dr Navina Evans and Marie Gabriel, told me how they had adopted a new mission two years ago. The new focus is on improving the quality of life rather than on symptoms.

This very broad mission and strategy are taking them into different territory where, alongside the provision of traditional services, they actively engage as partners with members of the local community to address issues of local concern. The wellbeing of the community matters to them whether working with local mosques or with West Ham Football Club, or dealing with the individual health issues of a particular patient.

They were talking very much the same language as the health creators in this book: broad, inclusive and not limited by organisational boundaries, and they were entrepreneurial in their approach. They told me that they were trying to move on from a situation where the different organisations just passed people between them. They wanted people to stop saying *'that's not us, its social services'* but instead ask how they could help.

It was the same welcoming approach of Bromley by Bow but also a recognition of their partnership with social care and that they wouldn't just pass problems on. At a deeper level it also reflected their belief that this was about peoples' rights and public ownership. The Trust had wider responsibilities and accountabilities and needed to behave accordingly.

The Trust has adopted the triple aim of improved population health, improved patient experience and improved value as its key measures of success. Like other trusts, it is only really measured officially on the last two areas – patient care and value – and their pursuit of the first measure, population health, doesn't really fit with the whole foundation trust regime.

This had led to the board having some difficult discussions about priorities. And Navina and Marie told me the biggest problem was that, despite the partnership arrangements it had in place, the Trust was really doing this by itself. The whole system hadn't yet changed. The Trust was constantly struggling to achieve its objectives and, at the same time, meet the more limited expectations of the NHS.

The Trust is not alone in the NHS in pushing at these boundaries, but it is clearly leading the way – offering a pointer for the future – and, as always befalls a leader, encountering new difficulties and challenges as it does so.

*****

New NHS Alliance, Bromley by Bow and Skelmersdale offer different perspectives on how the NHS can work with health pioneers locally. And the East London NHS Foundation Trust and the developments in primary care are examples of how people and organisations in the NHS are reaching out to work with local people and communities.

They are all creating the future and offering us pointers for what it is going to look like and how to get there. And it needs both parties, top down and bottom up, both hands clapping.

Some major issues stand out.

The NHS and government as a whole need to invest in building communities, and in those organisations that are engaged in spreading the learning and making sustainable change happen. Not by just supporting some bits of community activity as a means to a particular end and with short term and project funding. This point is picked up in the next chapter, but it is worth noting here that even exemplars as highly praised by government as the Bromley by Bow Centre are worrying about their sustainability.

The NHS needs to be more flexible and change its systems and regulations to support organisations such as the East London NHS

Foundation Trust, which is developing new approaches and ways of working with its communities.

The Department of Health and Social Care and all the other national bodies, such as Health Education England, the National Institute for Health and Care Excellence and the Care Quality Commission, need also to adapt their activities and approaches to support these new developments. Public Health England has supported several of the health creators, including Well North, and has a major role to play in the future. There is an opportunity here, too, for organisations like New NHS Alliance to work with other organisations active in supporting communities – C2 Connecting Communities, Incredible Edible and others – to learn together and accelerate change. Between them they have extensive networks of people with ideas and energy and who are already changing their communities. There is already a movement of people and ideas that could become a powerful *Movement* if there is the will and energy to do so.

Underpinning everything else, however, is the importance of attitudes and behaviours. As noted in the last chapter, it is not ultimately the policies, structures and systems that matter but relationships and mindset.

There is a danger that health creation could degenerate into just another thing the NHS has to do and there will be an explosion of tool kits and checklists about community engagement and health creation, which people will attempt to implement by rote. People need to engage personally, think about what they would do and not just follow the checklist.

How people behave, meeting people on their terms, and understanding their perspective are essential. It is why the Alliance's health-creating practices are so vital and why Health Education England and the schools, colleges and universities that educate health and care workers have such an important role to play.

***

There is also something missing. There is a long term plan for the future but, as yet, no truly compelling vision.

The NHS is going through a transformation from a hospital and doctor based system to a community, home and person based one. It is moving from an industrial model, where the patient moves through the system from primary to secondary to tertiary care and back again, according to set rules and processes, to a post-industrial one that has the person, their family and community at the centre, calling on services and support when they need it. From a linear system to a doughnut or life-ring approach with the patient at the centre.

Technology will help at every step, from prevention to treatment, and from logistics to interventions involving the latest discoveries and treatments. New technologies will be developed. Personalised medicine and targeted drugs. New understanding of how emotions and the social and physical environment affect health and wellbeing will feed into practice and therapies. And everything will be underpinned by AI and machine learning.

And people will be just as vital as today. People who can relate to us as individuals and to our families and communities. People like us.

Covid-19 has forced the NHS to change many of its services with more teleconsultations, greater co-operation between hospitals and with the private sector, and the development of new techniques and learning. There is also a renewed emphasis on staff safety and on recognising, as Chris Liddle pointed out in Chapter 9, that it is important to look after your people. They are key to de-stressing the situation and creating a safe and healthy environment for everyone.

These and other changes represent an opportunity to accelerate the changes and improvements already being made by the pioneers described in this chapter. Success will, however, depend on the will to change and on attitudes and behaviours. And on the sort of health-creating practices advocated by New NHS Alliance being adopted not just by clinicians but also by the managers, policy makers and politicians throughout the system.

CHAPTER FIFTEEN

WHAT THIS MEANS FOR GOVERNMENT

Health is made at home is all about action. It's about individuals, groups and organisations deciding to take an initiative. To lead. Deal with a problem they can see. Take responsibility. Take control of their health and their community. Act.

Sometimes this means going against current government policy. At other times the health creators are simply ahead of public opinion and the policy makers. But policy still matters. It can do damage, as austerity did, or enormous good as so many other policies have over the years in every field, from education and security to the environment and health.

Health can be thought about within many different frameworks: biological, epidemiological, psychological, sociological, economic, environmental, spiritual and others. All these frameworks offer insights and, I would argue, it is only by using them in combination that we can get a rounded or holistic view of health and of what needs to be done.

In recent years, debate on health has been very largely dominated by two broad and very different policy frameworks. One is an economic model concerned with costs, measurement, productivity, and individual health and healthcare – this is health as a business, which commoditises health and services and turns us into customers and consumers. The other is a much broader socio-economic one concerned with the determinants of health, society, community, population health, inequality, and social solidarity.

The first is a consumer model of health and the second falls within the long tradition of public health. This second model is also the territory of *Health in All Policies* which, as described in Chapter 12, is about ensuring that all public policy, whatever it concerns, takes account of the health implications. And, it requires an explicitly cross-departmental approach, so alien to normal government practice.

Both frameworks are important, although in recent years we have overindulged the economists and allowed them to take over the language of health – talking about supply and demand not needs and services, incentives not motivation, markets not populations, consumers not people. Language is important because it shapes and constrains our thinking. And this economic language makes it appear as if the economic framework is the only one that matters.

The socio-economic or social determinants framework, on the other hand, has not yet come into its own. As I have written elsewhere, understanding the way social structures and political processes affect health may ultimately be seen as being as important as the development of psychological techniques was a century earlier. This approach offers us new insights into health and healthcare.

The health creators described in *Health is made at home* come from many different backgrounds and perspectives. Most take a broadly holistic view of health that encompasses several different frameworks – psychological, social and environmental, for example. Several complain, as Marc Sansom does in Chapter 9, that government and other organisations they try to partner with take a very narrow view of health, work in silos and don't see the bigger picture.

Covid-19 has reminded us forcefully that there are trade-offs to be made. The most obvious is balancing safety, particularly of the most vulnerable, with sustaining the economy – when shrinking the economy will do its own damage to health, and lockdown means that patients with other conditions will have their treatments delayed. And governments also have to think about civil liberties, national unity, the impact on different communities and different regions, international relationships, and, as always, the mood of the public.

This chapter looks at how government works in practice and how its siloed departments and methodologies currently make it so poor at working on issues that cross these boundaries – and make it so difficult for organisations from outside to partner with it successfully.

The chapter concludes with the proposed changes to government policies that were identified in earlier chapters. These are representative of the types of changes needed if the pioneers and health creators are to be able to work more effectively with government in the future. They are only part of what is needed if the country is to learn the lessons from this pandemic and create a new vision and new future for the country. This is the most vital task facing the politicians and leaders from every sector of our country.

***

The current Government has been moving away from its policies of austerity since the 2019 election with some senior Conservative politicians being quite openly critical of it. And, of course, the Covid-19 pandemic has reinforced this change. However, the underlying government mindset, style and methods of operation will take far longer to change.

There has been for many years a sustained drive to make public services more efficient and accountable and, as is often said, more business-like. This is not in itself a bad thing. As NHS chief executive, I used competition in the NHS to break up cartels and bring about improvements, and I saw how making people account openly for their practice helped reduce variations in treatment that have damaged patients in the past. Sunshine, as somebody once said, sheds light in dark corners and is the best disinfectant.

And it is always important to have priorities. One of our priorities when I became the NHS chief executive was to reduce to zero the number of people who died waiting for a heart operation, and we targeted resources and effort on achieving it. Nobody disagreed and everyone was pleased when we reached our goal. This is partly the point, of course: who chooses and who agrees targets? Are they widely seen to be sensible or are they political or self-serving, or driven by a narrow concern for perceived efficiency rather than for effectiveness?

This managerial approach can be overdone, stifling creativity and taking away any sense of professional autonomy or ability to influence what happens. There seems to be almost no space left for exercising judgement. Badly chosen targets can miss the point. Poorly designed outsourcing can mean the loss of vital components of a service. Measuring the wrong thing can distort behaviour and damage outcomes. Naming and shaming can destroy confidence and with it any hope of real improvement.

I have seen the consequences of an overemphasis on these methods time and again in my journey around the country. I have seen schools exclude troublesome pupils because keeping them would damage their exam ratings. I have heard parents complain that social workers are just there to sit in judgement on them and there is no sense that they are there to support them. I also have heard health workers talk as if the purpose of the NHS is to save money.

This whole approach fits very well with the natural tendency of any government system, which is to centralise and give itself a sense of control. And this control is very unlikely to be given up easily, even if policies change.

There is an opposition here between the so-called business-like methods and business planning now central to government working and the entrepreneurial and inspirational leadership displayed by so many leaders in *Health is made at home*. Many senior politicians publicly declare their wish to see more entrepreneurial activity. But, at the same time, they want to see their departments deliver their top-down plans.

There is another dimension here too. Most politicians and civil servants have never run a business or, often, any kind of organisation and their approach is necessarily theoretical. Their natural territory is politics and policy and not practical delivery, understanding how things work and making sure they work in reality. These are very different skill sets.

It is no wonder that so many of the health creators whose approaches are encapsulated in the big ideas described in Chapter 13 – which emphasise relationships rather than systems, being entrepreneurial, experimental and learning by doing – find it so difficult to work with the NHS and government more generally.

This manifests itself in myriad ways. The researchers from Exeter University, who were evaluating the TR14ers described in Chapter 5, found that the standard research and evaluation methodologies used by government and the big funders simply don't work for these more entrepreneurial activities where people discover things as they go along and not as part of some pre-set plan. Richard Howells of the Tribe Project, described in Chapter 11, has found it enormously difficult to get government to act. And Andrew Mawson has had more than 30 years of trying to make change, despite the system.

It is often said that measurement is important because what is measured gets done. But what about things you can't truly measure like health and wellbeing, happiness, a good life and a good society? Or things that don't fit into one silo? Cross-cutting issues? Activities like those at the Bromley by Bow Centre, Incredible Edible or the Salford Dadz where they are doing things that fit in different ways into different government departments and across different areas of policy.

These are all examples of an overemphasis on the economic framework. Nothing shows this more clearly than the use and overuse of incentives – an economic term – to replace motivation. Do teachers and nurses really need to be incentivised to do their best for their pupils and patients? Some may do. But the emphasis here, as elsewhere, should surely be on supporting people to do what they believe needs doing and are passionate about – and on motivating them rather than incentivising them.

Government needs to create a new balance between the different frameworks. It needs to give more emphasis to socio-economic, psychological and environmental ones if it is to be able to work with the health pioneers and tackle the great health issues of our day, such as loneliness, stress, obesity, poverty and addictions. There needs to be more vision and values and less emphasis on business planning and performance indicators.

We still need accountability, efficiency and cost control, of course, but they are not the whole story.

And this new balance matters. This is not just a theoretical discussion about methodologies. It is about peoples' lives. Austerity with its economically inspired policies and political narratives of waste and blame damaged poorer people and communities, not the middle classes or wealthy. This has had profound effects on health, as researchers like David Stuckler, Sanjay Basu and Sir Michael Marmot have demonstrated.

The effects of austerity and the prevailing culture of public service delivery have, unsurprisingly, left people feeling they no longer live in a society that cares about them. They have done a great deal to destroy trust.

***

I have met many great leaders in the public, private and not for profit sectors who have risen above this culture to offer their people inspiration and, as importantly, create space for them to work to their potential and be creative. It is about passion and motivation. And authenticity.

Many far-sighted leaders are starting to create new narratives. Some private-sector leaders, as described in Chapter 10, have turned their companies into Certified B Corps, which means they explicitly consider the impact of their decisions on their workers, customers, suppliers, community and the environment. This is only a starting point, of course, for the leaders of social enterprises and community interest companies.

Looking to the public sector, it is very encouraging to read the comments of the Ofsted Chief Inspector Amanda Spielman, writing in her report in January 2020: *'We do acknowledge the role that strongly data driven accountability, including our own inspection frameworks, has played in distracting us collectively from the real substance of education.'*

I talked with Duncan Selbie, chief executive of Public Health England, about the work of his organisation. It was all about crossing sectors and government departments. He illustrated this by talking about the importance of children's speech and language skills to their readiness for school and their health.

'*The narrative is all about the economy, education, housing and place building,*' Duncan said. He went on to say that the biggest factor linked to ill health is level of income. And he is hopeful that the new Government's emphasis on the development of the North of England will lead to investment in jobs and the economy.

Andy Haldane, chief economist at the Bank of England and chair of the Government's Productivity Panel, has talked about the future being about '*infrastructure, innovation, skills and education, and about place and regions.*'

New ideas that have taken a long time in their gestation are now filtering through into the top of many influential organisations.

There is also a new focus on countries measuring happiness and wellbeing. New Zealand has become the first western country to introduce a *wellbeing budget* based on priorities including mental health, child poverty and family violence.

In the UK, Lord Gus O'Donnell, the former Cabinet Secretary and previously Permanent Secretary of the Treasury, has been actively promoting similar ideas. He and others have contributed to describing what this would mean in practice and helped establish the What Works Centre for Wellbeing. I spoke with Gus before Covid-19 struck and he wasn't very hopeful about progress within government. Now, however, in the changed climate of the pandemic, he is more optimistic that politicians and the public will understand the value of this approach.

In March 2020, as the virus really took hold, Lord Richard Layard, author of *Happiness* and co-editor of the *World Happiness Report*, reflected on the impact of the pandemic and wrote: '*I believe we are moving into a very different culture in which comradeship and co-operation are valued much more in comparison with interpersonal competition. And this can also be the moment when governments put the wellbeing of their people as their central goal rather than GDP.*'

The language used by politicians has certainly adjusted in this period to reflect the changed circumstances but whether this will be reflected in how government operates in the future is yet to be seen.

There is, however, clearly a new swirl of ideas and activity around different ways of thinking about government, growth and wellbeing. Some of this is reflected in the creation of new bodies like Action for Happiness. Much of it, of course, is revealed in the actions of the health creators all over the country, and in the great generous outpouring of voluntary and neighbourly action precipitated by the pandemic.

As importantly, leaders of some of our great national organisations like Ofsted, Public Health England and the Bank of England are setting out radical ideas and visions. There are people in leadership roles with whom the health pioneers can partner.

***

Looking forward, we are moving into an era when government will play an even greater role in all our lives and will be making major decisions that will have profound long term impact. It needs to be better equipped to do so.

Three things stand out from this chapter. Firstly, the Government needs to create a much broader vision for the country that goes beyond economics and the economic perspective. It should embrace the idea of policy making and measuring progress in terms of wellbeing. Secondly, it should work with the health creators to improve health and wellbeing in all areas of society, from employment and education to housing and the community. And, thirdly, it should introduce policies that promote health creation – encouraging and incentivising all sectors to take responsibility and create health – and aligning its own policies with this goal.

This chapter concludes by bringing together the ten important areas of government policy where change is needed, which were identified in earlier chapters. This is by no means a comprehensive list but it is indicative of the sort of changes that are required to build a healthy and health-creating society.

Between them they touch on most of the main areas of health creation. Not surprisingly, three are to do with children and another is about intergenerational fairness. Others are about employment, housing, social care and the environment. And two of them, in this deeply interconnected world, are about global relationships and planetary health.

We will see real change starting to happen if we implement these ten actions. The changes will be felt very widely within our society as they touch on almost all our lives. And, if they are to be successfully implemented, they will need government to change its own processes and mindset. These all cut across departments and depend on a different way of thinking about the world. Government will have to start thinking more like the health creators.

1. Review the impact of the zero hours and gig economy on health and wellbeing and introduce new measures to support and improve the mental and physical health of the workers involved.

There are millions of low-paid workers on zero hours contracts and in the gig economy, as noted in Chapter 3, whose organisations take little or no responsibility for their welfare. Very many workers are in a weaker position in bargaining and rights than they have been for years.

This is a very vulnerable group who have been made more vulnerable by Covid-19. And in recent weeks we have seen just how valuable many of them are, from the delivery drivers and cyclists to the farm workers and shop assistants.

2. Review and reform policy and practice on exclusion from school and implement changes as a priority.

Chapter 4 described the failure of government policies on exclusion from school and special schools. The way they are designed seems almost to guarantee that these children will be excluded for life, always on the outside, collateral damage in the campaign to improve our schools.

These failures have profound long term effects not least on our health system, where we will be paying the price for years to come. The NHS will be doing the repairs but it is powerless to deal with the underlying causes.

3. Review and change the Ofsted inspection system to ensure that its assessments focus on the real substance of education and not on achievement against necessarily narrow test results.

National policy underpins the whole education sector. And central to everything is the Ofsted inspection system. It has the laudable aim of improving standards but it has been widely criticised within schools for stressing and demeaning teachers and, very importantly in this context, taking attention away from anything such as health that is not included in its targets and measures.

As argued in Chapter 5, it is time to change the system.

4. Improve and increase the amount of vocational education opportunities available for children within the school system.

The concentration on academic subjects in schools and the pressure of testing and exams mean that a wide range of talents, strengths and passions are ignored or downplayed. As noted in Chapter 5, it is a very narrow gate that we expect all our children to go through. A system that, on the face of it, is all about encouraging success and achievement turns out, in reality, to be about stress and failure for too many.

There has been some movement in recent years with improvements in apprenticeships and a new requirement that all schools must offer pupils information about technical education. But more needs to be done to improve the opportunities for vocational education.

5. Introduce new policies on social care for the benefit of everyone who needs support.

As described in Chapter 7, the failure of successive governments to resolve the social care crisis is fundamental. The problems have been well rehearsed in public and yet still no action has been taken. Lack of financial support as well as facilities mean that thousands of people are stuck in hospitals who don't need to be there – blocking patient beds that could be used for people requiring healthcare – and many thousands more are trapped in their own homes with little or no support.

These problems are aggravated by the poor pay and conditions of so many carers: a largely forgotten and ignored part of the workforce – at least until now, where the pandemic has brought the importance of their work into sharp relief. Care homes have been very badly affected by the virus; in part, it seems, as a result of transferring patients to them from the NHS without enough attention to the impact on the homes. It is typical of the neglect of the sector over the years.

There needs to be wholesale change in the way care is provided and funded. Resolving this issue is long overdue and, however hard politically, must be a priority.

6. Support the Healthy Homes Bill and provide the political will to deliver the improvements in housing and planning that are so urgently needed.

In recent years, both building and design regulations have been relaxed, so there are no minimum standards, only a menu of options. The result is that, as described in Chapter 9, there are some very shoddy buildings being built and, even, office conversions where people are expected to live in rooms without windows. The size of rooms and houses are often much smaller than the Parker Morris standards that applied from 1919 to 1980.

As the Raynsford Review of Planning concluded: *'No system can be judged as 'working' if it cannot secure basic standards of light, space or places for children to play.'*

The pandemic has made this Bill even more important. Lockdown may have been a relatively pleasant affair for people with large houses and gardens, but millions have been trapped in accommodation that is inadequate, even at the best of times.

7. Support the Wellbeing of Future Generations Bill.

Government needs to be much better at long term thinking. There are many examples in *Health is made at home* where action today could head off longer term problems: from a better approach to excluding children from school to ensuring pensioners live in healthy homes. This short term planning damages people's health and lives and is more expensive in the long run.

Short term decision making has particularly acute implications for younger people. Too often, policy decisions are made without addressing the long term implications that they have on future generations. This Bill, as described in Chapter 10 and introduced in the House of Lords by Lord John Bird, will require public bodies to act to improve the environmental, economic, social and cultural wellbeing of current and future generations.

8. Embed the importance of planetary health within all government policies.

Planetary health refers to the health of human civilisation and the state of the natural systems on which it depends, as described in Chapter 10.

It links human health with the health of the planet and is about *'achievement of the highest attainable standard of health, wellbeing and equity worldwide through judicious attention to the human systems – political, economic and social – that shape the future of humanity and the Earth's natural systems that define the safe environmental limits within which humanity can flourish'.*

It will be vital to embed planetary health within all government policies and to bring together the work of different departments working on all related areas.

9. Convert its international development strategy into a co-development one, adopting the principles described here and, perhaps, renaming the Department for International Development as the Department for Global Development.

The industrialised countries of the West can learn a great deal about health from people in low and middle income countries who are, very often, forced to innovate and be inventive if they are to look after the health of their populations. There is also a great deal that they can learn from us. In the words of the Institute for Healthcare Improvement: *'Everyone has something to teach and everyone has something to learn.'*

As argued in Chapter 12, we need to start thinking in terms of co-development; where people from different countries and cultures work together on our shared issues. The whole language of international development with its top-down connotation of people from developed countries helping the underdeveloped is no longer appropriate. It must be two way.

10. Plan for the UK to become a global centre for health and health science.

The UK can play an enormous role in improving – and creating – health globally. It has deep expertise and remarkable networks and relationships worldwide, as noted in Chapter 12. The UK has world class universities and research, is a global leader in health policy and international development, has strong life sciences and biomedical and biotech industries, and has a vibrant and diverse not for profit sector.

It is already a world leader in health and should give this role even greater priority: planning for the UK to become a truly global centre for health and health science.

CHAPTER SIXTEEN

THE END OF THE LONG 20TH CENTURY

The historian Eric Hobsbawm's described 1914 as the end of the long 19th century. The First World War marked the end of the old order and the ideas and assumptions that had characterised the previous century. Four great empires fell during the war and new ideas were coming to the fore. Freud was writing his seminal works, the suffragettes were on the march, and the Bolsheviks took power in Russia.

We are once again in a period of transition when the world faces new challenges. And once again new ideas and attitudes are beginning to replace older ones.

The financial crisis of 2008 severely damaged western democracies and market based ideologies and helped shift global power eastwards. It brought austerity for millions in the UK and many other countries, helped widen inequalities and increased dissatisfaction with the ruling elites.

The Covid-19 pandemic is a far bigger human and economic crisis than the recession of 2008 and 2009. It may be seen in the future as the time when change vastly accelerated and we began to be able to discern the issues, ideas and assumptions that would dominate the 21st century.

Geopolitically, the US has abandoned world leadership and weakened its links with Europe at a time when European unity is threatened from within. We are at a moment, characterised as '*Westlessness*' by the Munich Security Conference, when the great western alliance that has for so long controlled global affairs is breaking up and we are forced to confront a multi-polar world where great powers with differing ideologies struggle for influence and supremacy.

Yet, it is also a time when climate change, economic stability, conflict resolution, mass migration and health demand greater unity of purpose and action globally. This applies across all areas of international activity. Most immediately for health, the role of the World Health Organization (WHO) is being questioned and there are conflicting demands from different countries for its powers to be expanded or reduced. The WHO is in the unenviable position of seeking to be the trusted adviser of all governments and, although the director general Dr Tedros Adhanom Ghebreyesus has pleaded with countries to keep politics out of the response to the pandemic, the WHO is inevitably being caught up in conflicts between member states. It is deeply depressing that this is getting in the way of fully co-ordinated global action. This will damage other health priorities, such as tackling antimicrobial resistance, and not just impede the response to the pandemic.

Globally, we are facing some very tough economic times when many national governments are likely to turn inwards and focus on economic and political survival. Civil liberties will be threatened, emergency powers imposed during the pandemic may be retained, and state surveillance of civilians could be increased. We are already seeing these things happen in countries in both the East and West.

On the more positive side, there are two big ideas about the future that were put forward pre-Covid and now seem even more relevant. The first is the idea that communities will become increasingly important.

Raghuram Rajan, the former governor of the Reserve Bank of India, has argued that human societies are built on three pillars – the state, the market and the community – and that the community has been neglected over recent decades and is due for a revival. Another distinguished economist, Paul Collier, sees the inclusive society as the model for the future. They and others writing about communities use differing definitions but all point to the importance of belonging, identity, culture, ethical frameworks and civil society. Communities, in other words, that can contribute to our health and wellbeing.

Several leaders and commentators also argue that we need a new focus on *human capital*, economists' jargon for people and their skills, knowledge and experience. Founder of Opportunity@Work Byron Auguste, for example, believes that *'skills, talent, tacit know-how, empathy and creativity'* are central to future success. Oliver Kamm, writing in April 2020, argues that investment in human capital will be crucial to economic recovery from the pandemic. He makes the related point that economic growth and productivity depend on how well new knowledge is assimilated by the workforce.

Many other writers have discussed how the workforce needs to change to meet the needs of the future, as robotics develop and as we grow accustomed to a much more 'virtual' existence. Many suggest we should add *caring* and *influencing* to Auguste's list of the key characteristics of the future workforce.

There is an enormous shortfall of health and care workers globally and it looks as if there should be scope to retrain some of the many newly unemployed people to fill the gap. American President Franklin D Roosevelt established the *New Deal* in the mid to late 1930s as a set of programmes, public work projects, financial reforms, and regulations designed to respond to the Great Depression. There is much talk in 2020 of the need for a new *New Deal* nationally and globally. Perhaps this one should involve massive investment and recruitment into the caring professions and public health. It would benefit the economy as well as the population.

Recent figures show a very large increase in people applying for nurse training since the pandemic struck. Maybe the public, as so often, are ahead of the politicians and policy wonks.

Government has provided financial support for people and enterprises throughout the country during the pandemic and will play an even bigger role for us all in the foreseeable future. It is an enormously difficult time but there are also extraordinary opportunities to build a new future for the country. The economist Mariana Mazzucato and others have shown that governments have a major role to play in providing the conditions for growing industries and creating economic growth. Visionary political leadership, purpose-led innovation and patient, research focused, long-view public funding have driven the growth of major industries in countries around the world.

The UK Government needs to move fast to create this vision and develop this new role while there is still a positive feeling of unity of purpose around the country and so much creativity being displayed by so many people – and before disillusion and despondency set in.

We simply don't know which of the many possible futures will prevail? Looking ahead, will opportunities be taken? Will we address climate change globally? Will we tackle inequality at home?

What, to adapt Hobsbawm's insight, are going to be the defining ideas that will be characteristic of the 21st century?

We can all, of course, play our part in creating a new and better society. The old normal was a cruel place for many people and we can do better. As a starting point, it is instructive to see how the health creators in this book have reacted to the pandemic. This is not speculation about the future but action in the present.

***

The health creators have all been very active. As I write in May 2020, all of them are continuing at least part of their work online; and most of them have found some way to contribute to the national and global effort.

Many have been hit by financial problems. Some charities like Horatio's Garden rely on open days and events to fund their activities, and some commercial bodies are heavily dependent on conferences and face to face contact. Hospices and charities as well as businesses have turned to the Government for help. Kami, a private company working in the area of postnatal depression, has had to cancel a funding round. Some groups have had to furlough staff.

And some groups have been badly affected in other ways. Baroness Jane Campbell of the Independent Living Strategy Group told me that she had received several reports that GPs were ringing their disabled patients and encouraging them not to go into hospital with Covid-19 symptoms and, during the phone call, asking whether they would like a *Do Not Resuscitate* notice added to their notes. She and others promptly organised an open letter, which resulted in NHS England issuing new guidance. It was, she says, '*a timely reminder to clinicians that blanket policies are unlawful and must not be used to guide treatment of disabled or elderly people, and that everyone must be treated according to individual clinical benefit*'.

This example illustrates how some groups have been disadvantaged by the emphasis on tackling the virus. Other problems and issues have been neglected. There are other worries, too, about surveillance and personal privacy, for example.

But despite all these obvious difficulties, the health creators have responded very creatively, protecting their communities and the people they serve, and starting new activities and services. The obvious headlines are about the use of IT and virtual meetings, events and messaging. Some, like HLM Architects, already had good IT facilities but they have had to adapt to run consultations with their clients online, some of whom were very unfamiliar with the technology. Others such as the FRUK forest schools are running virtual activities for the first time and *The Big Issue*, normally sold by street vendors, now has a subscription service with copies sent through the post.

Designers generally have been very creative, as shown by the many examples highlighted in the SALUS Covid-19 e-bulletin, which has provided a twice weekly round-up of recent developments. It has revealed extraordinary inventiveness in everything from modular hospitals and 3D printing of vital equipment to the redesign of road and transport systems. We need to understand how houses and communities can be designed for future when there may be more pandemics and more lockdowns – at a global, local and regional level. Our environment needs to be more resilient and adaptable.

More generally, of course, academia and industry have reacted very positively to the need for new equipment, research, tests and apps that allow us to understand and tackle the virus. And the Tribe Project is using its technology to play an increasing role in supporting local authorities, carers and community activities.

The biggest areas of activity are in supporting patients, carers and communities. Horatio's Gardens are still open for patients but social distancing rules are applied with volunteers coming in early in the morning to tend the gardens. The Charlie Waller Memorial Trust has increased its online support and information activity and is braced for more demand for its services. The City Mental Health Alliance is running virtual sessions and is very conscious of how its work will become more intense as a result of the virus. Poppy Jaman, its chief executive, was told by a partner in a global firm that *'75 per cent of partners attended the last mental health training call; 75 per cent of partners have never attended anything in all the time I have worked here'*.

During the lockdown Poppy has worked with the chief executives of other mental health charities to create the Mental Health Sustainability Fund. This is designed to improve the way they work together and engage the private sector in action on mental health and wellbeing. They are asking the private sector to donate skills, resources and funding and, in large part thanks to the links Poppy has made through the Alliance, they have launched the fund with a donation of more than £400,000 from Goldman Sachs. The aim is to sustain services and improve and protect peoples' mental health and wellbeing during and after the coronavirus pandemic.

The groups directly involved in health and in building communities, such as Bolton at Home and Incredible Edible, have adapted and developed their activities in response to the needs of their communities. And the Sewing Rooms has, naturally, started sewing materials for local health and care facilities. These and many other local groups have been playing a vital role in communities throughout the country.

Rob Trimble of the Bromley by Bow Centre told me: *'We have been busier than ever over the past six weeks. It's been like a revolution, without a few years of plotting and drinking coffee! The Bromley by Bow Centre has totally transformed its delivery model.*

'Alongside our usual extensive range of services (which have become virtual) we have added an on-site food distribution hub for 370 households in partnership with Bow Foodbank; created a new Crisis Social Prescribing service focused on 6000

vulnerable local residents identified by our primary care team; and formed a new partnership to provide much-needed bereavement counselling. We are now looking to establish a community based Covid-19 contact tracing service for our locality.'

'*The whole plan,*' Rob said, '*is called Thriving not just Surviving.*'

The benefits to be gained from nature, and from gardening in particular, have really come to the fore during the pandemic. The Royal Horticultural Society has been promoting the benefits of gardening for health and wellbeing for some years. And the National Garden Scheme (NGS), which arranges for private gardens to be open once a year to raise funds for nursing, has been actively promoting the health and wellbeing benefits of gardens since 2016.

In May 2020, in the midst of lockdown, the NGS launched Gardens and Health Week to promote the health benefits of gardens through films, broadcast talks and virtual tours. In doing so, it recognises that: '*At a time of enforced immobility and isolation for all, accompanied by great anxiety and personal tragedy for many, … gardens have been a powerful source of hope and positivity … People who would never call themselves keen gardeners have discovered that tending a few plants in a window-box, nurturing a houseplant or tackling that untidy back garden has transformed their mental state.*'

As George Plumptre, the NGS chief executive, says: '*Gardens … will unquestionably play a crucial part in the national recovery.*'

Other health-creating groups are actively supporting health workers from all backgrounds. THET, as described in Chapter 12, is running webinars and programmes for health workers globally, linking them for mutual support and learning. Nursing Now is bringing nurses together internationally to share experiences and promote solidarity. Many health workers, like the rest of the population, are experiencing new situations. Wearing personal protective equipment can be very isolating and many have been drafted into working in unfamiliar areas. And, as a nursing director of a private hospital group that was taking Covid-19 patients from the NHS told me, many of her nurses simply weren't used to looking after so many dying patients.

Working with Covid-19 patients is not only deeply traumatic but it can also be personally terrifying and, after weeks of this high tension existence, it is exhausting and debilitating. This is all made worse by worries about families and having to isolate when away from work.

Stephen Friend, whose research with sensors was described in Chapter 11, has started a study to understand how stress is affecting frontline workers. He is looking at the period between shifts and wants *'to follow the intense stress overwhelming frontline Covid-19 workers and how much they can recover while off shift. Eventually, such information might help prevent our healthcare workers going from susceptible to 'super-susceptible'.'*

It is too early at the time of writing to understand fully how different groups in the population are affected but it is already clear that people from black, Asian and minority ethnic communities are worse affected than the majority population, with people from black Caribbean backgrounds particularly hard hit. The reasons for the differences may well be multi-factorial and will surely include social issues about what jobs they do, their financial and other resources, and cultural issues.

I talked with Yvonne Coghill about this. She reminded me of our earlier discussion, described in Chapter 11, where she had explained how black people living in a white society were under greater stress, and how this affected their health and mortality. It may be that this is influencing their susceptibility to Covid-19. New research now suggests that the trauma of past generations, in the Holocaust or slavery for example, may affect the DNA and life chances of their descendants. More positively, Yvonne also told me that the NHS was about to set up a new health and race observatory, which would collect the data and accelerate our understanding – and our ability to act.

The pandemic has brought about massive and immediate changes in the NHS, some of which have been very welcome and some at least will have long term impact. The technological shift with virtual consultations and wider use of technology has attracted the greatest attention. But perhaps the most radical is the way that health and care have become increasingly integrated in practice.

Titilola Banjoko, executive managing director of Brighton and Hove Clinical Commissioning Group, told me that she was spending most of her time now working across the whole spectrum of health and care, supporting social care and care homes as well as hospitals and NHS bodies. It was about the NHS and the community. The danger is that these practices will slip back once the pandemic slows and the system reasserts itself.

I received very similar messages from other people working in health and care. The positive gains from the pandemic have been better teamwork, people working together on shared goals, speed of action and the use of technology. The NHS is actively seeking to hang on to the new good practices.

Navina Evans, chief executive of East London NHS Foundation Trust, has been appointed to lead the recovery plan across all NHS organisations in East London. She prefers to call it a reset in order to make it clear that the NHS is moving on and making progress. She reiterated many of the lessons that I have learned from the health creators in this book. So much progress depended on relationships, people knowing and trusting each other, on being entrepreneurial and on community support. Her trust, as described in Chapter 14, has adopted the aim of improving the quality of life for the population it serves. It proved to be exactly the right emphasis for responding to the crisis.

There are some positives to come out of this crisis. Other groups such as Bolton at Home and Unlimited Potential told me how much relationships with the NHS had improved and how important this was. But, as my discussions with Navina and others reminded me, there is a terrible toll of death, misery, delayed treatment, increased loneliness and isolation. The health creators are working to make something good come out of this awful time. A reset. Thriving not just surviving.

Globally, there will be many lessons to learn from the pandemic. Africa, where my journey started, has not as yet been hit badly by the pandemic. In part, at least, this seems to be because many countries have prepared well and have been able to build on their experience of other diseases such as Ebola. Matt Harris and colleagues writing in *Nature Medicine* have described some *'fast and frugal'* innovations that we can all learn from low income countries, ranging from the introduction of community health workers − local people who undertake health promotion and some treatment – to repurposing drugs and placing non-ventilated hospital patients in a prone position, lying on their front, to improve lung function.

Africa and other low income countries may, as mentioned earlier, be badly hurt by cuts in development funding and the neglect of other diseases during the pandemic. Organisations fighting TB fear that it has put back their work by five years and that, as a result, 1.4 million more people will die from TB. Others working on non-communicable diseases in low income countries are also very concerned about what is happening.

***

Government and the NHS need to change radically for the future.

In 2016, the *Lancet* published *A manifesto for a healthy and health-creating society*. I wrote it with 15 others, including some of the UK's foremost clinicians, scientists, academics, public health experts, civil society leaders and the editor in chief of the *Lancet*, Richard Horton. It argued for the UK to adopt four priorities.

The first was to recognise the importance of the health sector to the UK economy and to develop the country's leading role in health globally – for the benefit of the UK and the world. Funding the NHS properly, we argued, should be seen as an investment not a cost. No one now can surely doubt the intimate links between health and the economy.

The second was to accelerate the transformation of the NHS into a post-industrial, health and community based service, with investment in people and technology. This, too, seems clear as a result of the pandemic.

The third was to support health creation and the work of the pioneers, such as those described here. This, of course, is the purpose of this book.

The final priority was that *'health and care institutions should help develop and restore a healthy society in the UK'*. We argued in the manifesto that science and health bodies are important local organisations, which have a local role in tackling racism, promoting equality in all its forms, and celebrating innovation and creativity. I recall in our discussions that Richard made the explicit point that these organisations have a duty to promote scientific reasoning and objectivity, and should take a leading role in tackling fake news and pseudo-science.

The pandemic has brought science to our television screens and conspiracy theories to social media. There has never been a more important moment for these institutions to promote both science and objectivity. We argued in the *Lancet* that *'just as other sectors need to embrace health creation as part of their role, science and health need to embrace the development of healthy societies as part of theirs'*.

This is even more true now. And the health creators need to work with the NHS and government to build a healthy and health-creating society.

***

We are prisoners of our history and of the narratives and mindsets of our time.

I have been struck constantly by the way that debate about the NHS has for years been centred around the same old issues and on how much of this is based on models of production (or co-production) and on finance.

We have all become accustomed to using a reductive language. One that reduces everything to dry economic facts, measurements, simple plans, targets – the language of the market and the technocrat – and we apply it to everything we do. It is a 20th century language that has its uses but, as we have seen in earlier chapters, it has led to loss of motivation, growth of cynicism, and to the populism of simple solutions.

The stories in this book and the *big ideas* described in Chapter 13 are representative of a different way of looking at the world and of thinking about it. Our thoughts and language are what allow us to do things. They shape our world and our possibilities.

The work of the health creators – and the changes we are seeing during the pandemic – need to be supported by new narratives, new language and new evidence. They need stories to be told about them so that people understand what's going on, and they need intellectual underpinning.

We need a new language in which to think about the world. One that is characterised by all the big ideas here – community, control, meaning, learning by doing, design, the environment. Something kinder, based on relationships and that values mental health and wellbeing alongside physical health. And which isn't trapped in our old way of seeing the world, through the lenses of our NHS spectacles.

This doesn't mean challenging science or objectivity. There must be rigour, discipline and evidence in the use of the new language. We are already, for example, seeing evidence published in leading academic journals that meaning and social relationships improve health and wellbeing and that nature is good for us. And Michael Marmot and others have shown us that stress, loneliness and the social gradient damage health and shorten lives.

Nor does it mean that the language of economics is redundant. But it needs to take its place alongside the other frameworks. Part of a rich palette of ways in which we can see the world.

The idea of taking control – and of agency, autonomy, taking the initiative for ourselves, taking responsibility – is central to this whole new approach. Citizens and community should no longer be patient and passive.

Just as important is the idea of partnership, being an equal partner with the NHS and government in securing the constantly improving health and wellbeing of the population. We all have our role to play. Our responsibility.

***

What's the best we can hope for in the future – and work towards?

There are no complete answers. No Beveridge to give us a plan for health and society. We have to create the future ourselves.

Health is made at home has been a journey of discovery. It is a celebration of the thousands of people who are creating health and improving their communities. And it is an attempt to understand what they are doing and explore what this means for the future.

A few things stand out.

The health creation movement is here to stay. The health creators are unstoppable. They are creative, adaptable and determined.

Their approach and the ten big ideas we can learn from them are essential for building a better future.

Government needs to listen and learn – and be more accountable. The ten essential changes in policy identified here – dealing with issues as wide ranging as exclusion from school, healthy housing, planetary health and intergenerational fairness – can have an enormous impact.

The NHS needs to hang on to the gains from the pandemic, continue its transformation, play a full role in local communities, and learn how to work with the health creators.

And, it's time to act.

CHAPTER SEVENTEEN

CALL TO ACTION – FOR A HEALTHY AND HEALTH-CREATING SOCIETY

This book is about creating health. And understanding the causes of health.

The prevention of diseases is important but it's only part of the story. As described earlier, health and wellbeing are about so much more than the absence of disease. They are about life and freedom, confidence, and the quality of our lives. They are about our relationships, how we live, and what happens to us at work and at school. And they are about being all that we can be and living life to the full.

And creating health means providing the conditions in which people can be healthy and helping them to be so. It's what a parent does when they care for their child, helping them grow up to be healthy. And what a good teacher does. And a good employer. All of them exercising a profound and positive influence and helping create a resilient, confident, capable and healthy individual.

All of them are also helping build a healthy community. And we can't be truly healthy ourselves unless we are part of a healthy community, a healthy society and a healthy planet.

These ideas echo throughout the book. Free Range Urban Kids are growing up stronger and healthier in their forest school. Poppy Jaman is helping employers improve mental health. Pam Warhurst and Gary Stott are creating kinder, more confident, connected communities. Andrew Mawson brings people together locally – businesses, not for profits and the public sector – *'joining the dots'*. John Bird is giving homeless people a *'hand up'*. And, in the NHS, Navina Evans and Marie Gabriel have focused their NHS foundation trust on improving the quality of life of local people.

Each of these is only one part of a much bigger story where people around the country are making improvements and creating health.

***

Health is made at home is a celebration of health creation and the health creators.

There is a great movement of people and organisations creating health and, at the same time, taking on the system and challenging the traditional ways of doing things.

They are showing us that it is time to change the way we think and talk about health. To focus on health creation and the causes of health. And to start locally in the home, the workplace, the school and the community.

And they are showing us that it's time to recognise that we can't leave our health and wellbeing entirely to the NHS, the professions and the politicians. Everyone has a role to play and a responsibility to do so.

Time to act decisively. To create health and not just do the repairs.

And time to bring everyone and every organisation that affects our health together in the great shared goal of building a healthy and health-creating society.

***

The Covid-19 pandemic has reminded us of the courage and skills of health and care workers, and of the great value of the NHS and the wider care system.

It has reminded us that governments have far-reaching roles in providing for the health as well as the prosperity and security of the nation – and that these three are very closely interlinked.

It has also reminded us of the deep divisions in our society of wealth and opportunity and race. And of the tensions and conflicts around the world that thwart international collaboration and present enormous risks to us all.

Looking forward, the future is very uncertain with the world facing a major financial crisis and the NHS needing to deal with a long tail of waiting lists and increased mental health problems for the public and health workers alike. There are very difficult times ahead.

***

Now, however, with the world disrupted by the pandemic, is the right time for us to act. We need to create a new partnership between the health creators, the NHS and government, making the most of the strengths and skills of each partner, and focused on building a healthy and health-creating society.

The partnership needs to be based on three clear points. Firstly, the NHS and government simply can't tackle today's major health problems such as mental health, obesity and addictions by themselves. They can only hope to do the repairs. Everyone from every sector of society – all of us – has a role to play and a responsibility to do so.

Secondly, the NHS and government should explicitly recognise the importance of creating health – and the lessons we can learn from the health creators – and focus on it alongside their other vital roles in disease prevention and service provision.

Thirdly, the partnership needs to build on the understanding that the health of each of us depends on the health of the community, the nation and the planet. It needs a joined-up approach across sectors, silos and timescales.

And the partnership must learn from the health creators about the importance of relationships; communities; taking control for ourselves;

building on strengths; connecting and communicating; tackling mental health; having meaning and purpose in life; a healthy environment; being entrepreneurial and learning by doing; and taking off our NHS spectacles to see the world anew.

And health professionals can adopt the health-creating practices advocated by New NHS Alliance – listening and responding, truth-telling, focusing on strengths, helping people self-organise, and shifting power.

This partnership must be about shared vision, behaviour, mindsets, focus and, above all, practical action – and not grand plans, systems and organisational change that will clog up the system for years to come.

Health is made at home ends with a call to action for each of the three partners: the health creators, the NHS and the Government.

The health creators need to find better ways of working together. Individually they are impressive, but together they could be an enormous force for good – changing the way we think about health and how the NHS and government work. They have many different perspectives and skills and there are enormous opportunities for synergy, joint action, sharing information and networks, building momentum, and influencing the national agenda.

They are already making a start. Some of the leading health creators will be participating in a series of public webinars on building a healthy and health-creating society following publication of this book, in the summer and autumn of 2020. They include Well North Enterprises, The Big Issue, Incredible Edible, New NHS Alliance, SALUS, the Bromley by Bow Centre, Vertical Future, the Tribe Project, Brightness Management, C2 Connecting Communities, HLM Architects, the Black Health Initiative, the City Mental Health Alliance, Charlie Waller Memorial Trust, Unlimited Potential, the Oracle Partnership, the National Garden Scheme, and the Town and Country Planning Association.

The NHS needs to work with the health creators to maintain the improvements made during the pandemic in areas such as working across organisational boundaries, using technology and speed of response. There are many excellent examples, some described in this book, which, if retained, will help the NHS accelerate its transformation into a health and community based system.

Even more fundamentally, the NHS needs to embrace the idea of health creation and include it in a new and broader vision of creating a home and community based health and care system. This will give it a renewed focus on local communities and on relationships with local organisations, businesses and agencies in the shared endeavour of creating health and improving the quality of life.

The Government, too, needs to set out a new vision that recognises the importance of health and wellbeing alongside the economy and security, and confronts the divisions and inequalities revealed by the pandemic. It, too, needs to focus on quality of life, local communities and the causes of health and wellbeing.

As importantly, it needs to change the way it works, moving away from a central planning and *one size fits all* mentality to identifying and working with local entrepreneurs, the health creators and others who are making improvements in their areas. Money will be very tight and needs to be spent where it will have most effect.

And the Government should introduce policies that promote health creation – encouraging and incentivising all sectors to take responsibility and create health – and aligning its own policies with this goal.

It can start in a very practical way by adopting the policies in the ten areas identified in this book: support for people on zero hours contracts; exclusion from school; reform of Ofsted; vocational education; social care; healthy homes; intergenerational fairness; international co-development; planetary health; and establishing the UK as a global centre for health and health science.

Each and everyone of us has our part to play in building a healthy and health-creating society.

CONTACTS AND FURTHER READING

Chapter 1. Introduction
Marmot M: The health gap – the challenge of an unequal world; Bloomsbury, London, 2015

Marmot M, Allen J, Boyce T, Goldblatt P, Morrison J: Health equity in England – The Marmot Review 10 years on; The Health Foundation, London, 2020

Valuing carers 2015 – the rising value of carers' support – see https://www.carersuk.org/news-and-campaigns/news/unpaid-carers-save-the-uk-132-billion-a-year-the-cost-of-a-second-nhs

Chapter 2. Taking off our NHS spectacles
Crisp N: Turning the world upside down – the search for global health in the 21st century; CRC Press, London, 2010

Chapter 3. Good for the business and the right thing to do
The City Mental Health Alliance's website http://www.citymha.org.uk

Mind's mental health at work website https://www.mind.org.uk/workplace/mental-health-at-work

Stevenson D, Farmer P: Thriving at work – a review of mental health and employers; DWP and DHSC, London, 26 October 2017 – see https://www.gov.uk/government/publications/thriving-at-work-a-review-of-mental-health-and-employers

The Whitehall Study – see
https://unhealthywork.org/classic-studies/the-whitehall-study

Chapter 4. Exclusion, aspirations and achievement

Path Hill Farm's website https://www.pathhill.com

Cranbury College's website http://cranburycollege.reading.sch.uk

Chapter 5. The pressure to be perfect

TR14ers' website http://www.tr14ers.org.uk

C2 Connecting Communities' website
https://www.c2connectingcommunities.co.uk

Ofsted annual report 2018/19, published January 2020 – see
https://www.gov.uk/government/collections/ofsted-annual-report-201819

Charlie Waller Memorial Trust's website https://www.cwmt.org.uk

North West Training Council's website https://www.nwtc.co.uk

Chapter 6. Free range children

FRUK's website https://freerangeurbankids.com

Forest School Association's website https://www.forestschoolassociation.org

Good Play Guide's website https://www.goodplayguide.com

KAMI's website http://www.usekami.com

Me.Decoded's website https://www.medecoded.com

Sure Start – see https://www.education-ni.gov.uk/articles/sure-start

The Early Intervention Foundation's website https://www.eif.org.uk

The Early Years Collaborative – see
https://www.nes.scot.nhs.uk/education-and-training/by-theme-initiative/
child-health/programme-information/early-years-collaborative.aspx

Chapter 7. Meaning and purpose in later life

Gray M: Sod 70! – the guide to living well; Bloomsbury, London, 2015

The Sewing Rooms' website http://www.the-sewing-rooms.co.uk

Pizzo PA: A prescription for longevity in the 21st century – renewing
purpose, building and sustaining social engagement, and embracing

a positive lifestyle; Journal of the American Medical Association, Chicago, 9 January 2020, 2020: 323(5): 415-416. doi:10.1001/jama.2019.21087

U3A University of the Third Age's website https://www.u3a.org.uk/

The Challenge Hub's website https://www.thechallengehub.org/

All-Party Parliamentary Group for Longevity: The health of the nation – a strategy for healthier longer lives; London, February 2020 – see https://appg-longevity.org

Worldwide Hospice Palliative Care Alliance's website https://www.thewhpca.org

The Lancet Commission on Palliative Care and Pain Relief – see https://www.thelancet.com/journals/langlo/article/PIIS2214-109X(18)30082-2/fulltext

Frome Compassionate Community – see https://www.compassionate-communitiesuk.co.uk/projects

Maggie's Centres' website https://www.maggies.org

Dementia Services Development Centre at University of Stirling's website https://dementia.stir.ac.uk

Public Health England: Community-centred public health – taking a whole-system approach; January 2020 – see https://assets.publishing.service.gov.uk/government/uploads/system/uploads/attachment_data/file/857029/WSA_Briefing.pdf

Chapter 8. Joining the dots in the community

Bolton at Home's website https://www.boltonathome.org.uk

UK Men's Sheds Association's website https://menssheds.org.uk

The Commission to review the provision of acute inpatient psychiatric care for adults: Old problems, new solutions; Royal College of Psychiatrists, London, February 2016

Salford Dadz Little Hulton's website https://www.salforddadzlh.org

Unlimited Potential's website https://www.unlimitedpotential.org.uk

Incredible Edible's website https://www.incredibleedible.org.uk

Mawson A: The social entrepreneur: making communities work; Atlantic, London, 2008

Chapter 9. Design and the environment

Horatio's Garden's website https://www.horatiosgarden.org.uk
HLM Architects' website https://hlmarchitects.com
Housing LIN's website https://www.housinglin.org.uk
The Housing our Ageing Population: Panel for Innovation (HAPPI) report 2009 – see https://www.housinglin.org.uk/Topics/type/The-Housing-our-Ageing-Population-Panel-for-Innovation-HAPPI-Report-2009/
The TCPA's website https://www.tcpa.org.uk
The Healthy Homes Act campaign – see https://www.tcpa.org.uk/support-the-healthy-homes-act
The Raynsford Review of Planning: Final report; TCPA, London, November 2018
van den Bosch M, Bird W (Eds): The Oxford textbook of nature and public health. The role of nature in improving the health of a population; OUP, Oxford, 2018

Chapter 10. Sustainability and planetary health

Agenda-setting foresight – the Oracle Partnership's website https://oraclepartnership.com
Safeguarding human health in the Anthropocene epoch: report of The Rockefeller Foundation–Lancet Commission on Planetary Health; July 2015 – see https://www.thelancet.com/commissions/planetary-health
The Sustainable Development Goals – see https://sustainabledevelopment.un.org/?menu=1300
Vertical Future's website https://www.verticalfuture.co.uk
Social Enterprise UK's website https://www.socialenterprise.org.uk
The Big Issue's website https://www.bigissue.com
Certified B Corporations' website https://bcorporation.net/about-b-corps
The Bank of England's regulatory approach to climate change – see https://www.bankofengland.co.uk/climate-change

Heseltine M: Empowering English cities; Haymarket Media Group, London, 2019 – see https://englishcitiesmichaelheseltine.premediastudio.com/MichaelHeseltine/page_1.html

Smith A: An inquiry into the nature and causes of the wealth of nations; London, 1776

Well-being of Future Generations Bill [HL] 2019 – see https://services.parliament.uk/bills/2019-19/wellbeingoffuturegenerations.html

Well-being of Future Generations (Wales) Act 2015 – see https://futuregenerations.wales/about-us/future-generations-act

Chapter 11. Taking control of our health

Bronze Labs' website https://www.bronzelabs.co.uk

The Tribe Project's website https://tribeproject.org

Community Catalysts' website https://www.communitycatalysts.co.uk

4YouandMe's website https://www.4youandme.org

Workforce Race Equality Standard – see https://www.england.nhs.uk/about/equality/equality-hub/equality-standard

Black Health Initiative's website https://blackhealthinitiative.org

Harrow International Christian Centre's website https://hicc.org

Chapter 12. Global action

THET's website https://www.thet.org

THET's principles of partnership – see https://www.thet.org/principles-of-partnership

Marlborough Brandt Group's website https://www.mbg.org

Zambia Anaesthetic Development Program – see https://www.salg.ac.uk/sites/default/files/ZADP-BLOG.pdf

Britnell M: In search of the perfect health system; Red Globe Press, London, 2015

Britnell M: Human – solving the global workforce crisis in healthcare; OUP, Oxford, 2019

World Health Organization: Alma Ata Declaration on primary healthcare; Geneva, 1978 – see https://www.who.int/publications/almaata_declaration_en.pdf

World Health Organization: Helsinki statement on Health in All Policies; Geneva, 2013 – see https://www.who.int/healthpromotion/conferences/8gchp/8gchp_helsinki_statement.pdf

Omaswa F, Crisp N (Eds): African health leaders – making change and claiming the future; OUP, Oxford, 2015

Skopec M, Issa H, Harris M: Delivering cost effective healthcare through reverse innovation; British Medical Journal, 2019: 367. doi: https://doi.org/10.1136/bmj.l6205

Harris M, Marti J, Watt H, Bhatti Y, Macinko J, Darzi A. Explicit bias toward high-income country research: a randomized, blinded crossover experiment of English clinicians; Health Affairs, 2017: 36(11): 1994-2007

Health Education England, global engagement – see https://www.hee.nhs.uk/our-work/global-engagement

Nursing Now's website https://www.nursingnow.org

World Health Organization: The state of the world's nursing 2020; Geneva, 6 April 2020 – see https://www.who.int/publications-detail/nursing-report-2020

Crisp N, Brownie S, Refsum C: Nursing and midwifery – the key to the rapid and cost effective expansion of high-quality universal health coverage; World Innovation Summit for Health, Qatar, November 2018 – see https://www.wish.org.qa/summits/wish2018/forums-research-chairs-2018

All-Party Parliamentary Group on Global Health: The UK as a global centre for health and health science; London, 5 February 2020 – see http://www.appg-globalhealth.org.uk/reports/4556656050

Chapter 14. What this means for the NHS

NHS England: The NHS Long Term Plan; London, January 2019 – see https://www.longtermplan.nhs.uk

NHS England: NHS Five Year Forward View; London, October 2014 –

see https://www.england.nhs.uk/wp-content/uploads/2014/10/5yfv-web.pdf

New NHS Alliance's website https://www.nhsalliance.org

New NHS Alliance's five features of health-creating practices – see
https://www.nhsalliance.org/health-creation

The Coalition for Collaborative Care's website
http://coalitionforcollaborativecare.org.uk

The Ideas Alliance's website https://ideas-alliance.org.uk

The Health Foundation's website https://www.health.org.uk

NHS Horizons' website http://horizonsnhs.com

Collaborate's website https://collaboratecic.com

Bromley by Bow Centre's website https://www.bbbc.org.uk

St Paul's Way Transformation Project – see
https://amawsonpartnerships.com/st-pauls-way-transformation-project

Well North Enterprises' website https://wellnorthenterprises.co.uk

Social prescribing – see
https://www.england.nhs.uk/personalisedcare/social-prescribing

East London NHS Foundation Trust's website https://www.elft.nhs.uk

Chapter 15. What this means for government

Stuckler D, Basu S: The body economic – why austerity kills;
Basic Books, New York, 2013

New What Works Centre for Wellbeing – see
https://www.gov.uk/government/news/new-what-works-centre-for-wellbeing

World Happiness Report – see https://worldhappiness.report

Action for Happiness's website https://www.actionforhappiness.org

Mazzucato M: The entrepreneurial state. Debunking public vs private
sector myths; Penguin Books, London, 2018 (new edition)

Chapter 16. The end of the long 20th century

Munich Security Conference report 2020, Westlessness – see
https://securityconference.org/en/publications/munich-security-report-2020/

Rajan R: The third pillar – the revival of community in a polarised
world; William Collins, London, 2019

Collier P: The future of capitalism – facing the new anxieties; Allen Lane, London, 2018

Opportunity@Work's website https://opportunityatwork.org

Kamm O: Investment in human capital will be crucial to economic recovery; The Times, London, 17 April 2020, p33

Royal Horticultural Society's website https://www.rhs.org.uk

National Garden Scheme's website https://ngs.org.uk

Harris M, Bhatti Y, Buckley J, Sharma D: Fast and frugal innovations in response to the Covid-19 pandemic; Nature Medicine, London, 11 May 2020. doi: https://doi.org/10.1038/s41591-020-0889-1

Crisp N: Everyone has a role in building a health-creating society; BMJ, 19-26 December 2015, p26-27 – see http://www.bmj.com/content/351/bmj.h6654.full?ijkey=vJlVsZNrBSvE6Fz&keytype=ref

Crisp N, Stuckler D, Horton R, Adebowale V, Bailey S, Baker M, Bell J, Bird J, Black C, Campbell J, Davies J, Henry H, Lechler R, Mawson A, Maxwell PH, McKee M, Warwick C: Manifesto for a healthy and health-creating society; The Lancet, London, 7 October 2016. doi: https://doi.org/10.1016/S0140-6736(16)31801-3

Chapter 17. Call to action – for a healthy and health-creating society

For more information, visit https://healthismadeathome.uk

ACKNOWLEDGEMENTS

I am very grateful to the many people who have talked with me about their work and their ideas over the last year. It has been a real privilege to learn about what they are doing. I greatly admire their creativity, passion and determination – perhaps the three most important qualities they all share.

It has been particularly inspiring to see how these pioneers and health creators have reacted to the pandemic, learning fast, adapting their approach and staying true to their vision and aims.

I have discussed ideas about creating health and social change over many years with a number of people including Andrew Mawson, Jane Campbell, Yvonne Coghill, Victor Adebowale, Phil Freeman, Chris Liddle, Penny Jones and Eldryd Parry. Each of whom, from their own different and distinctive perspectives, have helped me to understand the world better.

I have been influenced by the pioneers of the social determinants of health and 'Health in All Policies' including, naturally, Michael Marmot as well as Ilona Kickbusch and Martin McKee, and by the great public health doctors Muir Gray, Harry Burns and John Ashton. I have also learned a great deal from people with specialist knowledge of different areas including Janet Sutherland, Jeremy Porteus, Hugh Ellis, Heather Henry, Hazel Stuteley, Merron Simpson and Brian Fisher.

Looking globally, I am indebted to African friends including Francis Omaswa, Miriam Were, Sheila Tlou and Tedros Adhanom Ghebreyesus, and to others with a global overview including Lincoln Chen, Srinath Reddy, Julio Frenk, Felicia Knaul, Maureen Bisognano, Don Berwick, Richard Horton, Ben Simms and Mark Britnell.

SALUS Global Knowledge Exchange has been an excellent publisher, with the added advantage of being able to contribute its own specialist health knowledge. Andrew Sansom has edited the book with great skill and flexibility. I am very grateful to Joanne Fenwick and Laura Clarke for the excellent design work. And Marc Sansom has led the whole project with great imagination and judgement while coping with the demands of running a business during an epidemic.

As always, my wife Siân has been my most important adviser and support. Her knowledge of anthropology, education and the environment and her insights have made this a better book.